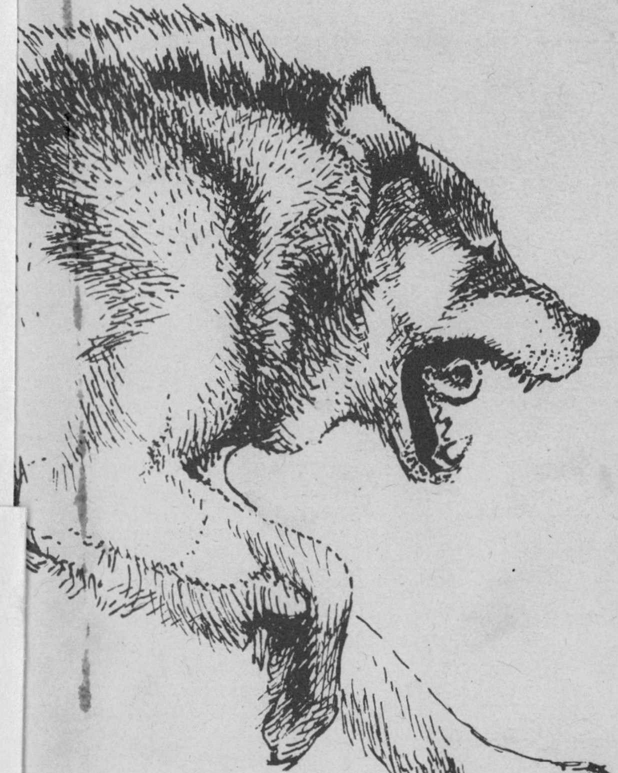

the
order of
WOLVES

the
order of
WOLVES

Richard Fiennes

Bobbs-Merrill
Indianapolis / New York

Published by the Bobbs-Merrill Company, Inc.
Indianapolis/New York

Published in Great Britain by Hamish Hamilton Ltd

ISBN 0-672-52141-5 Hardcover

Library of Congress Catalog Card Number: 75-39952

Produced by Walter Parrish International Ltd, London
Designed by Judy A. Tuke

Printed and bound in Great Britain by Purnell & Sons Ltd,
Set in Plantin 110 11 on 12 pt

First U.S. printing

to GERALDINE and ROSANNA

Contents

Preface

During years gone by, man has committed many atrocities both against his own species and against those animals which share the earth's habitats with him. Belatedly, he has begun to take stock of himself and to judge the consequences of his actions. This is not to say that he has been universally destructive. Attempts have been made throughout the ages to preserve animals that have been threatened; mostly it must be said for the sport of hunting them, although the Père David deer was saved from extinction by some forgotten Chinese emperor. Nevertheless, many more animals have become extinct by man's action than have been saved, particularly those which compete with him for earth's dwindling resources. Sometimes, this has been done for obvious reasons. Elephants are controlled because they trample plantations; baboons root up the ground-nut crops; rabbits eat the produce of the vegetable gardens. With other animals, their destruction is encompassed in blissful ignorance of the true nature of the animal or of the consequences.

For thousands of years, man's hand has been turned against wolves, partly because of their depredations on domestic stock, but as much because wolves are held in mortal fear. They are believed to attack human beings and devour children, and to be associated with the powers of darkness. It is only recent studies which have shown what amicable and indeed lovable creatures they are. A great deal is now known of their ways of life, which is not known outside the world of biologists. I hope that this book will introduce to a wider public the truth about the ancestors of our domestic dogs, and, in so doing, assist the efforts of those who urge the conservation of wolves and wish to see an end put to their mindless destruction by brutal methods.

The material in this book is based on the devoted researches of a relatively few field workers, who have studied wolves and their habits, and on the records of hunters and trappers, who have lived in proximity to them. Acknowledgement of their work has been given in the text and the bibliography.

The presentation and production of the book were the responsibility of the Walter Parrish organisation; I am greatly indebted to those members of the staff who have given so much time and trouble to it.

Richard Fiennes

A portrait of the wolf

Among the northern peoples of the world the wolf has become a legend and a symbol. In legend, he is associated with strange acts such as the suckling of Romulus and Remus, were-wolf traditions, and other unusual traits of behaviour. He is a symbol of savagery, ferocity, and courage.

There are in fact many subspecies and varieties of wolves, which live in different habitats, and betray different forms of behaviour. The wolf of tradition is the northern grey wolf, *Canis lupus*, the type species of the genus, and his close cousin the timber wolf of North America. Throughout recorded history, man's hand has been against the wolf. His very name arouses thoughts of war, of snowy wastes, of blood-curdling howls, and of packs of fierce animals that will attack and devour defenceless wayfarers. His name provokes thoughts of Napoleon's armies in retreat from Moscow, flanked and attacked by these outrageous beasts, the weak and wounded being torn to pieces. Perhaps we think of Hitler brooding in his Wolfschanze in the mountains of Bavaria, and plotting conquests and destruction of all mankind except his own particular thugs. We recall tales of Red Riding Hood and of the Big Bad Wolf. Predatory males are wolves, that prey on defenceless young women, and their hunting cry is the wolf whistle.

During recorded history, indeed, man and wolf have been antagonists and rivals. In Great Britain, the rivalry ended by the early 18th century in the extermination of the wolves. Throughout the rest of Europe and parts of Asia, they have been harried and driven from their haunts. In America, they have been unceasingly persecuted and to this day are hunted by helicopter and light aircraft, and ruthlessly destroyed by automatic weapons. Even in the Arctic countries, their hold on existence is precarious. Belatedly, scientists have begun to question the rationale for wolf-extermination and to study the true nature and habits of these animals. Whereas in days gone by the

Timber wolf, North American representative of *Canis lupus* and the same species as the grey wolf of northern Europe, resembling most closely those of eastern Siberia. His ancestors probably migrated to the American continent when it was still joined to Europe by a land-bridge.

A she-wolf and two of her young family—there may be up to six cubs in a litter.

propriety of eliminating a large and supposedly dangerous predatory animal was not called in question, many scientists are now examining their consciences and there is a widespread movement, particularly in the United States and Canada, to promote the conservation of wolves. Indeed the subject has become highly emotive and in state legislatures tempers rise in exchanges between the protagonists of conservation and extermination. This is not surprising, since the true facts of wolf lore are so difficult to unravel from the numerous stories and tales that are told about wolves, from the deeply rooted prejudice of man against them, and because of the difficulty of making real studies of the habits of so elusive an animal.

Both in Canada and in the United States, particularly in Alaska, properly controlled scientific studies of wolf habits have been mounted, from which much valuable information has emerged. Even so, such surveys are mostly confined to studies of wolves in a single, perhaps rather specialised habitat, and they give a single viewpoint. Their authors, in discussion of their results, mostly reject accounts of the experiences of the older hunters, who lived in close proximity to wolves, as anecdotal and unsoundly based. Such an attitude is unnecessary and pedantic, and in studying the wolf problem one should surely seek to appraise the experiences of early. times and to glean from them such information as is of definite value. For example, the opportunity no longer exists to study the habits of the 'buffalo wolves' which preyed on the great herds of bison before they were virtually exterminated. For the wolf adapts his habits and ways of life according to the habitat in which he lives and according to the prey which is his source of food. A true picture of the wolf cannot, therefore, be obtained by a study of the species in one particular situation, and it is essential to use with discrimination all the records available.

The wolf's tragedy is essentially a matter of ecology. Wolves are animals of wide open spaces, evolved to hunt the great herds of grazing animals that during the Ice Ages migrated seasonally north and south over the great snowscapes of the Arctic countries. In open country, prey cannot be captured by stealth, so that superior speed, or cunning and social organisation, must be developed if success is to be achieved. However, no predator has developed speed superior to prey animals; evolution keeps the prey always one step ahead. Accordingly, the two great predators which emerge in Ice Age times, wolf and man, both developed a high degree of social organisation and communication and greatly enhanced intellectual powers. Wolves can produce a useful turn of speed over relatively short distances; man on the other hand lacks these physical powers and became entirely dependent on his organisational ability.

In Ice Age times, however, man existed only in small nomadic bands and there was no scope for rivalry between man and wolf. Indeed, they may to some extent have complemented each other. Man, by cunning stratagems, would frequently kill great masses of animals, in pits or by driving herds over cliffs, acquiring far more food than he could use. Moreover, he would normally consume only the more tender and choicer portions of the carcass, since, without cooking, his teeth and masticatory apparatus could not cope with much that wolves could consume. It is therefore likely that some wolves relied for a part of their diet on man's leavings; they would trail along close to human hunting parties, just as they did in the days of the early buffalo-hunters in North America. There was evidently in those days a form of mutual respect between these two predatory animals, and man had not developed the feelings of fear and horror which later beset him. The early buffalo-hunters had no fear of wolves, nor today in what remains of the Arctic wastes do the Eskimos fear wolf attacks. It is only in Eskimo country that the old relationship between man and wolf can still be studied; yet until very recently almost no attempt was made to elucidate Eskimo wolf lore. One fascinating record is that of Farley Mowat in his witty little book *Never Cry Wolf*. But the modern research scientists discount his book as largely fictional and valueless.

By 10,000 years ago, the ice had receded far to the north. It had formerly extended as far as the Thames and the Alps in Europe, to the Himalayas in Asia, and to Arizona in the New World. The land, which had formerly been open and suited to the hunting methods of man and wolf, became largely closed with dark, impenetrable forests, and both wolf and man were forced to adapt their ways of life to the new situation. The wolves took to the forests and preyed on forest animals, but food was always scanty for them and they were forced to make forays beyond the forest limits in order to obtain sufficient for their needs. Man, on the other hand, did not penetrate the forests, but lived on the forest fringes and along the seashores, from which he obtained shellfish and other fruits of the sea. Some 10,000 years ago, he began to domesticate animals. He took into captivity and bred the wild hairy sheep, the mountain goats, the wild boars of the forest, the reindeer of the Arctic North, and the giant forest ox—the aurochs. He also captured and tamed wild horses, which roamed European and Asian steppes in large numbers.

Is this why wolves are feared? Note the deadly trap-like tooth arrangement—once locked on to his prey, the wolf never lets go. Yet a healthy wolf never attacks man.

These animals were also hunted by the wolves. It was beyond the capacity of the wolves to distinguish between wild stock and domestic, which were in any case much easier to catch. Early pastoralists were faced with depredations on their flocks by wolves hunting singly, in pairs, or in packs; hence antagonism and rivalry arose. Indeed, certain wolf stocks were themselves domesticated, and their progeny used as guard dogs against wolves; they were even trained in later years as wolf-hounds to hunt them. Wolf and man now became ecologically incompatible, and with ecological incompatibles one or other has to go. The wolf went, and is still going. So strong became the tradition of the wolf as a thing of evil in certain societies that the instinct to destroy him still activates much human behaviour.

When the ice receded, forest cover was by no means universal, and there appeared also the great prairies of grass which spread over the black chernozem soils of North America through Asia to the Black Sea region. These prairies supported large herds of grazing animals,

such as saiga antelope, bison, and particularly horses. In these areas, both man and wolf could continue their hunting activities in much the same way as before. Man, however, had become a nomadic pastoralist, owning his own herds of domesticated cattle, horses, sheep, and other animals. On these herds, the wolves preyed and took a certain toll, even as they do today in Central Asia, where these depredations do not appear to be greatly resented and losses are comparatively small. Strangely, the wolves often take dogs from the settlements and small villages of the nomads. Even in the days of the early settlers who hunted buffalo in North America, wolf and man were not in rivalry and coexisted on amicable terms. It was only after the mass destruction of the bison and the introduction of domestic cattle that rivalry arose and steps were taken for the extermination of the unfortunate wolves, forced to prey on the domestic stock by the destruction of the bison, their normal livelihood.

Rivalry was most acute in the countries of western Europe, such as France, Spain, and the British Isles. In these countries, when populations were comparatively small, most settlements were in the valleys, while the hills remained forested and uninhabited. It was in the hills that the wolves lived, and from which they made their sorties to prey on the livestock of the farmers. The situation was particularly serious in a country such as Scotland, where virtually the sole wealth of the people rested in their sheep and cattle. Vigorous attempts were made to exterminate the wolves, but these were largely unsuccessful until their habitats were destroyed by elimination of the forests.

The old relationship between man and wolf, one of fellow predators in open country complementing the activities of one another, thus became one of fear and distrust, felt so widely and so strongly by human peoples. Meanwhile, what became of the attitude of wolves to man as a result of his altered relationship? Did wolves indeed change their attitude? Did they become savage hunters of man? Did they attack and devour lonely wayfarers, whom they could waylay?

Certainly, it was widely believed that they did, and in remote areas refuges were constructed where travellers could take refuge at night from wolf attack. We must confine ourselves here to the northern grey wolf, since the habits of the Asian wolf of India and elsewhere may be different.

The answer is extremely curious. In spite of numerous tales to the contrary, there is no authentic record of any human being ever having been attacked and killed by a normal healthy northern grey wolf. Reports of attacks by wolves on man in Europe are numerous, though very rare in America. Most of the European tales come from Scotland, France, Spain and the Ukraine, and concern wolves preying on domestic stock and being hunted. It is possible that the

European and American wolves differed in their habits in this respect, but most of these tales refer to incidents which occurred hundreds of years ago and the truth cannot now be verified; nor can the probability that the wolves involved were in fact rabid. One early English writer, Josselyn, in his *New England Rarities Discovered* (1672), wrote as follows:

> . . . wolves are not man kind (that is they would not attack human beings), but do much harm by destroying of our English cattle.

Most of the North American stories are remarkable for the fact that the attacked hero beat off the wolves attacking him, an impossible feat if the wolves were bent on business. One gentleman claimed to have beaten off a wolf with his hat! There are, indeed, many tales of men being at the mercy of wolves and coming to no harm. For example, Abert in 1848 described how a snow-blinded member of his hunting party was left in camp. Wolves surrounded him, but did

In time the wolf became almost a mythical creature —men regarded him with fear, even horror, reflected in tales and fables handed down over the ages. The were-wolf legend is just one.

A wolf engraved 'for the sportsman'—a hunter may approach a trapped wolf quite safely. Wolves used to hunt the great bison herds on the prairies of North America; when they were forced to prey on domestic cattle, all means were used to kill the wolves, including poison and traps, so that they are now extinct in many southerly areas.

him no harm. As late as 1928, when the wolves were being persecuted, Barbour described how a hungry wolf stole his fish when he was asleep and defenceless, but did not attack him. Farley Mowat, too, had his preconceived ideas of the merciless ferocity of wolves shattered when on two separate occasions he found himself confronted by wolves a few yards away—they observed him with interest, but did not attack him.

Wolf cubs stolen from the parents when only three or four months old are readily tameable, docile and affectionate. However, they vary greatly in temperament and some remain resentful and savage, never becoming reconciled to captivity. These are presumably the ones that would in natural conditions become the future pack leaders, and find a position of subordination intolerable.

The Asian wolves (*Canis lupus pallipes*) are very different from the northern wolves, though their hunting methods are similar. Though they hunt in packs over the plains, they often enter villages in India and—it appears—will indeed steal human babies, which they kill. It is said that they are dangerous and will attack human beings found in a defenceless position. Even so, the young reared in captivity show the same love and affection for human beings as do northern wolves and domestic dogs.

Where attacks have been made on man by northern wolves, the animals have almost certainly been suffering from rabies, a disease which not infrequently affects them especially when their population tends to become excessive. Even a hunter who has a wolf in a trap can safely approach him; the wolf exhibits social signs of submission and submits quietly to whatever fate is in store for him. This behaviour is characteristic even of the lonely wolves, the so-called 'loners', whose mates have all been destroyed, who have been ruthlessly hunted, and who have by supreme cunning over many years avoided attempts to destroy or capture them. Furthermore, as the Eskimos know well, a man can safely enter a wolf's den and steal the cubs, while the parent wolves stand at a distance and watch with resignation. This behaviour is the more strange because wolves, although they normally eat carrion only when there is little alternative, readily unearth human corpses and devour them. This is well known from early records in countries such as Scotland, where cemeteries were removed to wolf-free islands off the coasts, and from reliable North American records. It is difficult to account for this behaviour in a predatory animal without entering realms of fantasy.

Wolves have highly developed social senses, observe a rigid etiquette among themselves, and obey and respect the leader of the pack. At some stage an old leader may be challenged by a younger wolf and deposed. A wounded wolf is frequently set on, killed and eaten. Yet man is never treated in this way.

The origins of wolf and man

When a drastic change in the ecological conditions of the northern parts of the world changed the relationships between wolf and human populations into antagonism and rivalry, man developed a fear and distrust of the wolves, which led him to exterminate them. The wolves fought a losing battle for survival. To some extent, man atoned for his sins against wolves by bringing some sections of them into domestication as the domestic dog. In this situation their complementary powers were of value to each other, and the wolf progeny contributed materially to human welfare. The wolf's near-idolatry of man showed in the fierce attachment of the dog to his master. We must go back further to see how ecological conditions brought into being the wolves themselves with some very strange characteristics, which were nevertheless adapted to the situation of their lives; and how man, too, evolved and came to be one of the wolf's fellow predators in the Arctic tundra.

The earliest mammals appeared on earth, according to the fossil record, some 150 million years ago during the Mesozoic era, when the great reptiles were dominant on earth. Reptilian dominance lasted 100 million years and only ended some 60 million years ago, so that the mammals coexisted with them as an undistinguished and unimportant class for as long as 90 million years. The reasons for the sudden and massive reptilian extinctions are still not properly understood. Many scientists attribute them to changes of the earth's climate and topography; but there is no certainty and it is odd that the aquatic reptiles became extinct at the same time as the terrestrial. This is one of earth's great mysteries. But with the disappearance of the reptiles there was left an ecological vacuum, of which the humble mammals took quick advantage.

During the era of reptilian dominance, the ancestors of the mammals, although they had existed so long on earth, failed to evolve in such a way as to compete with the reptiles. They are distinguishable from them only because their lower jaws were formed

The common ancestors of man and the chimpanzee, shown here, had to develop differently from the wolf's forebears, to adapt to life in the great tropical forests.

of a single bone, whereas the jaws of reptiles proper had three. Their brains were very small, no larger in proportion to body weight than those of the reptiles from which they were descended. They were probably covered by hair or fur, evolved from the reptilian scales. This would be an adaptation for the maintenance of body-temperature, since they had become warm-blooded. Nevertheless, temperature control would be rather primitive, so that they would need to hibernate during cold seasons. They laid eggs, as do the most primitive mammals still existing, the monotremes—duck-billed platypus and echidna. Their tooth structure shows that they lived largely on insects. Nevertheless, their teeth show the characteristics of mammals, being differentiated into incisors, canines, premolars and molars.

Here was a blue-print for the mammals of today, but their further advance was not possible until the earth's habitats favoured them. To maintain a high body-temperature requires more food and more frequent feeding. Whereas the reptile can feed every few days only and stay in a state of torpor, the mammal needs a continual intake of energy-producing foods. In this sense, the warm-blooded animal is less efficient and less competitive, unless other compensating advantages are developed. The expansion of the mammals involved the evolution of a great variety of types to take advantage of the habitats vacated by the reptiles. Thus, these little insect-eating creatures produced widely dissimilar groups, adapted to different types of habitat and to different ways of life.

At that time, the tropics were warm and humid, supporting great belts of tropical forests north and south of the equator. Some primitive mammals therefore took to the trees in pursuit of the abundant insect life which flourished there. They were the ancestors of the primates, the group to which man himself belongs. Animals which resemble the ancestral primates still exist on earth—the tree shrews. From some such animal came the prosimians, the monkey-like creatures which resemble monkeys, but are not yet quite monkeys. We see them today in the bush-babies and lemurs to be found in most zoos. From them came the true monkeys and the great apes, the so-called Hominoidea. And from an early branch of the Hominoidea came the stock ancestral to man himself. Man came when, with climatic change, the extent of the tropical forests became reduced and his ancestors were forced to live on the ground, a habitat to which he was entirely unsuited. However, let us see first what qualities he had developed as a result of his arboreal existence.

The successful tree-living animal requires rather special properties. He must be equipped with limbs capable of grasping the branches of the trees, so the fingers become long and prehensile. He must be

The lemur of today is rather like the prosimians through which man is descended.

Later in the story came monkey-like creatures resembling the rhesus monkey. Later, when the forests diminished, man's forebears had either to become extinct, or adapt to life on the ground; whereas wolves were natural predators in open country, and fit better into the ecological scene.

The origins of wolf and man

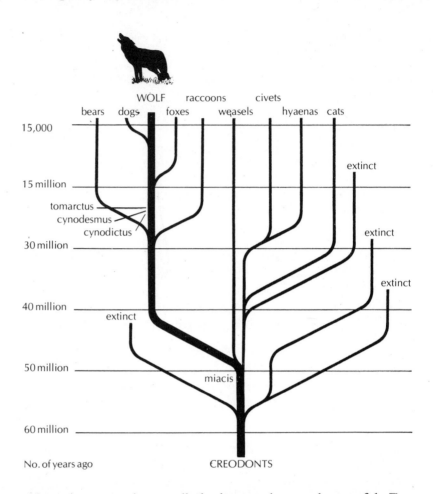

The evolution of the wolf. Wolves emerged late in evolutionary terms as specialised hunters in open country.

able to jump, so the rear limbs become long and powerful. For locating prey, the sense of smell is of little use in the light and wayward forest breezes. So the scent organs tend to be diminished and the senses of hearing and sight become more acute. Thus, the muzzle becomes shorter, and the orbits and the eyes become larger. Furthermore, precision in locating the exact position of hand or footholds becomes important, and so binocular vision is developed. The eyes become frontal instead of lateral. These changes result in the development of the typical primate physiognomy. However, for locating other members of the species or group, some form of communication is necessary. In the forest, they cannot be seen at a distance and so a system of calls comes to be developed; as time goes on, these calls by variation and modulation come to have some meaning, such as warning of danger, location of food, readiness to mate and so on. From this development comes social organisation, so that monkeys move around in troops. The development of the troop requires order, so that hierarchies are developed.

24

All these developments demand an increase in nervous control of the systems involved. The control of vision in the brain is located close to the cerebral hemispheres, the centre of reasoning and intelligence; the centre which interprets olfactory sensation is on the periphery of the brain. Manual dexterity demands an increase in the nervous mechanisms which control it. The interpretation of sounds demands intelligent analysis. Thus, the primate brain became much enlarged and there occurred the beginnings of that increase of brain power which has had its culmination in the human ability to forecast, plan, and reason. At the same time, in an arboreal habitat there are few predators. A few snakes slither into the trees. An occasional eagle may pounce. In the lower branches, perhaps a leopard or other feline may be able to attack, but the danger is not great. The primates, including man's ancestors, thus lost their weapons of defence. Their teeth, particularly the great canines, became reduced to such an extent that they no longer constituted a menace. The limbs, too, became poorly suited to fast movement in flight from predators on ground surfaces.

Man's ancestors, therefore, when forced to adopt a terrestrial, instead of an arboreal, existence were singularly ill-equipped to cope with the situation. They had no defence against predators and could not even move over land surfaces fast enough to escape them. Monkeys, such as baboons and patas, were also forced to the ground and re-developed dangerous offensive teeth, and in the case of the patas became endowed with considerable mobility over the ground. Not so man's ancestors, who coped with the situation by the use and development of their higher intellectual powers, their superior social organisation, and their capacity to adapt to new situations. It is paradoxical that these powers had been developed as a result of their past arboreal existence. From being largely vegetarian, these apes began to hunt animal food, firstly small creatures, then, as their expertise increased, larger prey. They learned to trap small ruminants, and used clubs to despatch them. They then began to fashion weapons from wood, and bone, and stone. Man the tool-maker was emerging. These skills demanded a further increase in mental powers, which led to the control of fire, the building of shelters, and other skills which were the forerunners of civilisation. Yet, none of this would have been achieved without a yet greater improvement in social organisation and powers of communication. So, from it came speech and from speech the powers of abstract thought, religion, and the communication of abstract ideas.

Man's ancestors, now man and not apes, as a result of these powers spread widely over the earth, from Africa to the Far East, though his numbers were small and he existed in small nomadic bands. He lived as a successful predator, capturing small and large animals with traps and killing them with his weapons. To the end of the Pliocene, he was well adapted to his new environment, though natural selection through the ages must have taken a terrible toll of his numbers to eliminate those unfitted to it. However, when the Pliocene gave way to the Pleistocene, there occurred a new climatic change in the northern hemisphere, which again threatened the survival of these representatives of the human race in more northerly areas. The Ice Age descended, and the face of the earth was changed. This Naked Ape had to learn to hunt the great animals that roamed the icy wastes or perish; he must warm himself or perish; he must eat the flesh of large animals, for which his tooth equipment was inadequate. He used fire to warm himself and he learned to cook his food; he made steam baths by pouring water over red-hot stones; he hunted fur-bearing animals, including wolves, to provide warm clothing; he adapted his life to the new situation. In this new habitat, he found himself, with the possible exception of the cave hyaena, the sole predator on the snowscape, except for the wolf.

As the supreme paradox of human development, when the ice receded, during the intervals in the Ice Age and when it ended, man had become so well adapted to this environment that his survival was again threatened, and the spur to civilized development was applied. So, wolf and man came to cohabit on the snowscape, and to hunt the same animals. How then did the wolf develop?

When the first mammals began to emerge from the reptilian stage, this left behind the egg-laying monotremes. The marsupials, the kangaroo family, became an offshot of the mainstream; they evolved to bring forth live young, but at a very immature stage. The other mammals, known as the placental mammals, evolved to produce fully developed young. Even so, some remained rather primitive, like the insectivores—the hedgehogs and moles—and the edentates—the armadillos and ant-eaters. There was another group, destined to sire both the great herbivorous and carnivorous groups of mammals, which spread over the whole of the earth. The ancestral carnivores are represented by a group of fossil mammals, known as Creodonta; the ancestral ungulates form a group known as the Condylarthra. However, the early members of the two groups were scarcely distinguishable from each other. It is another of the paradoxes of evolution that from the same insect-eating ancestors, one group should have come to subsist on a solely vegetable diet, and that the other should have come to prey on them.

At that stage of earth's history, the land was very flat and the climate was warm and moist. There were great areas of swamp vegetation, vacated by the reptiles. Nature demands a primary producer. All life stems from the energy of the sun, trapped by the plants in the process of photosynthesis, and some animals—if there are to be animals—must consume this and convert it into animal flesh. Without these primary producers, there can be no predators to advance the food chains. To become the dominant fauna of the earth, the mammals had, therefore, to produce from among their stock some group which would exploit the abundant vegetable material. The herbivore and carnivore groups gradually diverged to produce the characteristic fauna we know today.

Because of the swampy nature of the ground, the herbivorous animals were first evolved with splayed feet, which had small pads like a dog's; these were suitable for wet ground and they did not sink into the earth. The swamp vegetation, on which they fed, was soft and their teeth were rather weak and low-crowned, for browsing on fruits and soft leafy material. Yet, the characteristics seen in our modern herbivores were beginning to develop; the legs were becoming more rigid for rapid movement and flight from predators and the numbers of toes were being reduced to allow for faster movement. The ancestral horses, for example, had three functional toes on each foot, the central one being the largest. They had come also to walk and run on the toes; that is, they were digitigrade as opposed to plantigrade—walking on the soles of the feet. The carnivores, on the other hand, remained plantigrade. They were small animals, like weasels, which hunted by stealth and cunning, creeping through the swamp vegetation and taking their prey by surprise. The herbivores were at that time quite small—even the ancestral horses were little bigger than large rabbits, though with longer legs.

The most primitive form of locomotion is plantigrade (walking on the soles of the feet) as in bears, above. Digitigrade locomotion (on the toes) as in horses and wolves, below, gives more speed.

The wolf is one of the great predatory order of Carnivora, descended from common, unspecialised ancestors rather like the weasel. Many such carnivores, unlike the wolf, hunt by stealth, catching their prey unawares.

The extinct woolly rhino, which shared the wolf's prehistoric terrain. We do not know if wolves could tackle so formidable a foe, but in northern Canada and Alaska they will kill the musk ox, almost as great a challenge.

However, a new age was to dawn with another climatic change and a drastic alteration of the topography of the earth. There were great cataclysms, in which continents split apart, mountains were upthrust, and the climate became drier and colder. As a result, great stretches of grassland were developed over an enormous area of the earth's surface, across what is now central U.S.A., through Siberia into Europe and on to the shores of the Black Sea. Grass, though a wonderful food for herbivorous animals, is tough and fibrous, and the seeds contain abrasive siliceous materials. No animal lacking specialised teeth and digestive equipment can use it for food. Teeth become worn away, and the tough cellulose of leaf and stem can only be assimilated by special organs of digestion. Some groups of the herbivores were evolved to exploit this new source of food. The low-crowned (brachydont) teeth become high-crowned (hypsodont) presenting plate-like grinding surfaces, subject to continuous wear through life. In order to digest a great bulk of fodder, the digestive system developed great fermentation chambers, such as the rumen of the artiodactyles, or the capacious caeca of horses.

These arrangements tend to make the animals heavy and lumbering, and impair their chances to escape predators. For this reason, many groups became much larger and developed horns and other weapons of defence and so became formidable adversaries. Others, such as the horses, developed long legs, large hearts and strong muscles so that, in spite of the heavy digestive apparatus, they retained a fleetness of foot by which they could escape across the prairies from their attackers. Yet others, such as the rhinoceroses and elephants, became so large and their skins so thick that no predator could tackle them. Plains-living herbivores in this way became virtually immune to attack. In the forests, animals could still be hunted by stealth and forested areas abounded in predators of the cat and allied families, which hunted in this way. On the plains, animals could rarely be hunted by stealth and, because of their size, they were still endowed with a speed sufficient to outstrip predators and, if cornered, with means of defence with which to protect themselves.

28

It was not until the end of the Pliocene, when the Pleistocene Ice Ages swept over the earth, that predators emerged capable of dealing with this situation. The successful predator had to tackle a prey animal very much larger than itself. It must be able to waylay and isolate the victim from its herd. It must have a sufficient turn of speed over a sufficiently long distance to catch the prey once isolated. It must have teeth adapted to seize the prey and hold on to it, until it could be brought to the ground and killed.

Such an animal was evolved in the ancestral wolves, first found in late Pliocene fossil deposits. They were rather small but by the Lower Pleistocene wolves of very large size were to be found, larger even than the northern wolves of today. The gait became digitigrade instead of plantigrade and the limbs were lengthened, giving the greater turn of speed. The jaws and muscles of the head became greatly developed to accommodate a fearsome tooth armoury. Most important of all, the wolves developed, as did man, a well-organised social system and higher intelligence, which enabled them to hunt in packs and outwit the prey by attacking from different directions and laying ambushes. While man remained slow-moving, but had unusual dexterity to make and use weapons, the wolves became swift-moving and had their own natural offensive weapons—their teeth. Man was far more sagacious and deadly: his offensive armoury consisted of weapons, which were effective from afar, as bows and arrows, javelins, feathered darts and so on. He learned to plan stratagems by which his prey animals could be corralled or caught in traps. To withstand the Arctic climate, the wolves developed great cold resistance and magnificent thick pelts, and could sleep in the open in Arctic temperatures. Man, on the other hand, was forced to provide himself with warmth by making clothing of animal skins and using fire. Man was a more efficient hunter and could take from the herds the best of the animals; the wolves never became more than scavengers of the herds, living on the sick, the weak, the injured, and

The Canadian wolf's tireless lope, some 6 mph, which he can maintain for hours on end, sometimes covering 40 miles in a single night.

	ERAS	PERIODS		AGE Million Yrs.
PHANEROZOIC	CENOZOIC		Epochs	
		Quarternary	Recent	
			Pleistocene	
				2.5
		Tertiary	Pliocene	
			Miocene	
			Oligocene	
			Eocene	50
			Paleocene	
	MESOZOIC	Cretaceous		100
		Jurassic		150
		Triassic		200
	PALEOZOIC	Permian		250
		Pennsylvanian = L. Carboniferous		300
		Mississippian = E. Carboniferous		
				350
		Devonian		400
		Silurian		
		Ordovician		450
				500
		Cambrian		550
CRYPTOZOIC	PROTEROZOIC	Metazoans		600
	ARCHEOZOIC	Fungi		2300
		Blue-green Algae		2700
		First Traces of Life (Bacteria)		3300
		Origin of the Earth		4500-5000

This summary of the geological calendar shows how recent the Pleistocene is in evolutionary terms. The column on the right gives approximate ages in millions of years.

the very young. Man's depredations were ecologically serious, and he has been blamed for the extinction of the mammoth and of horses in North America. The wolf's inroads on the herds were never serious, and indeed were ecologically beneficial by removing the weaklings and thus improving the quality of the stock itself.

Strangely, the Ice Age produced conditions ideal for the development of vast herds of grazing animals. The forest cover was reduced, and the melting of the ice in summer meant that great areas of open land, well-watered from the melting snow, provided an enormous amount of suitable fodder. The earlier days of the Pleistocene produced the mammoth, the woolly rhinoceros and great herds of other grazing animals, some of then now extinct. During the Upper Pleistocene, there were species which survive to this day—bison, reindeer, caribou, elk, musk ox, and horses. Massive herds roamed north and south according to season, feeding on the lush vegetation. During the intermissions of the Ice Age, numbers of both man and wolf dwindled. The Ice Age habitat was to their liking; when it disappeared, the spread of forest hampered their activities. And so it was at the end of the last Ice Age between 20,000 and 10,000 years ago.

Thus man and wolf met on the tundra plains, pursuing the same prey in different ways. The wolf was a natural denizen of the habitat, evolved to take his part in the ecological scene. Man was forced into it by ecological changes, which denied him the habitat for which he evolved and to which he was suited, an outcast from his own home, an intruder on an ecosystem to which his ways were not adapted. For both, their ideal habitat was largely destroyed when the ice receded. Both were resilient; the wolf capable of adaptation to the new situation. Man could only adapt himself to it by modifying the

The musk ox, prey to the wolves in the Pleistocene Age, and still in existence today.

The mammoth—like the woolly rhino, a companion of the wolf in early Pleistocene times, but destined to disappear.

Opposite, the characteristic sight of a howling wolf, a northern wolf from Baffin Island in Canada.

habitat and to a great extent destroying it, giving rise to the chain of events which has culminated in the world scene as we know it today.

These two groups of animals shared one asset, intelligence and social organisation in advance of anything evolved in other animal groups. In other ways, they were totally dissimilar. What man possessed—keen sight, manual dexterity, the power to make weapons, and to plan ahead—the wolf had not. What the wolf had—keen scent, fleetness of foot, powerful tooth mechanisms, and the ability to rend the toughest meat and crush bones—man had not. They evidently supported each other even if, as may be supposed, there was not some form of commensal alliance. When the habitat changed, this alliance continued between dog and man; the wolf was domesticated and his powers were used by man to supplement his own. In the next chapter we shall try to understand the Ice Age habitat, which brought these two allies together and which was their home for hundreds of thousands of years.

The home and
community of the wolf

The wolf achieved his maximum development during the glacial period, or great Ice Age, which provided the open conditions which best suit his hunting methods. The Pleistocene Ice Age was interrupted by two short and one long interglacial periods, in which the climate became warm and temperate or even subtropical. During these interglacials, the fossil records show that wolf numbers became diminished, while they were greatest when the ice reached its furthest point. At its most extensive, the ice is believed to have reached a southern limit more or less corresponding in England to a line joining the Severn Estuary to the Thames Estuary; this is shown most clearly in the well-known boulder clays of East Anglia, which convincingly prove that the country was invaded by ice from the north. Among the boulder-clays are found rocks which originated in Norway and were carried to East Anglia by the advancing glaciers. On the American continent the ice reached what is now Nevada.

These early Pleistocene deposits contain fossil material from a number of mammalian species now extinct, including the so-called sabre-toothed tiger and two species of elephant. There are also flint implements, evidence of occupation by Palaeolithic man. With the return of warmer weather, there appear the remains of animals such as hippopotamus, indicating that conditions were really very mild. However, these are succeeded by mammoth, reindeer, musk ox, and Arctic voles with the return of very cold Arctic conditions.

The term tundra, as understood today, indicates the barren wastelands beyond the furthest limit of trees in the Arctic region of North America and Asia; the word is derived from the Finnish, meaning 'land without trees'. In these areas, the summer lasts only two or three months and the temperature does not at any time exceed 50° Fahrenheit. The winter is long and severe, and the sun does not shine throughout the mid-winter months. However, precipitation is not very heavy and snow does not lie deep; in places

The tundra is not as barren as we might imagine—in spring there are flowers such as those here in the foreground.

35

it is entirely swept away by the icy winds. The subsoil is permanently frozen (permafrost); the top layers thaw in the brief summer, creating cold and damp conditions, but there is no integrated system of streams to carry off the water from the melted snow and so it lies in hollows forming icy pools and swamps.

In these conditions the vegetation is of necessity shallow-rooted and low and, except in some specialised sections of the habitat, no tree growth is possible. In most places the vegetation consists of hummocks of moss which grow in a dense mat on raw, acid, peaty humus. In some places dwarf shrubs grow, such as willow and birch, and small-leaved, evergreen plants like bilberry, crowberry, and stunted rhododendron. Where the drainage is better there is some grass and on south-facing slopes attractive 'bloom-mats' of flowering herbs such as aconite, geranium, willow herb and forget-me-not. The Arctic regions, surprisingly, support a rich fauna. The mammals, wolves apart, include foxes, hares, lemmings, caribou or reindeer, and musk ox, all of which manage to support themselves on the rather sparse vegetation. For the smaller mammals, the snow provides an insulating layer in which they can burrow, and under which plant roots and seeds are preserved as a food reservoir. During the summer migratory birds are especially numerous, and in spite of the large distances they have to fly they mostly arrive in a fat and healthy state. It is in these areas that they mate and breed, feeding, as the thaw sets in, on mosquitoes which appear in large numbers, both the larvae and the adults providing a source of food for the bird populations. The birds also eat willow buds and crowberries. A permanent resident of the Arctic tundra is the ptarmigan, a bird which is adapted to Arctic conditions and able to feed on the Arctic vegetation.

The tundra is, in fact, divided into two areas, that which is permanently frozen and that from which the snow and ice recede in summer and where the attractive vegetation described then appears. It is this that provides most of the fodder for the great herds of caribou and reindeer which migrate seasonally north and south as it becomes available to them. Today, as we shall see, the wolves with their exceptional intelligence have learned to exploit almost every type of food that is offered—bird life, rodents, berries, and the large game which they hunt in packs.

What conditions were like when the tundra extended far to the south, to the Thames and Severn Estuaries, to the Himalayas, the Alps, and New Mexico, is hard to visualise. At that time, there occurred rain ages or 'pluvials'. The whole of the Sahara and other great deserts in the northern hemisphere were well watered, supporting rich vegetation and numbers of grazing animals. In the north

The strange beauty of the tundra.

36

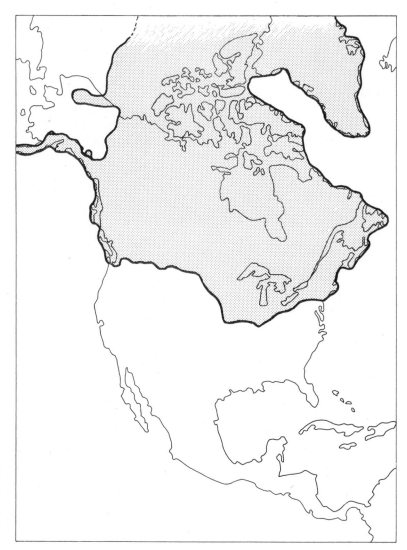

On this page and opposite, the extremes of glaciation in America and Europe. Far south there developed a typical Ice Age fauna in which wolves and man were the main predators. Their adaptation to it was so exact that survival problems arose when the ice receded.

Britain was joined to the continent of Europe by land, and Asia to America by a land bridge from the Bering Strait as far south as the St Lawrence. Grazing animals could roam from continent to continent and the wolves could go with them. The summer thaw was clearly very extensive, and there is evidence that bands of human hunters ranged far to the north of their winter quarters in search of game, even as far as Scandinavia. Wolves, in these conditions, extended north from a point as southerly as the Caucasus. They ranged over an enormous area of the earth's land surface and, although their territorial demands were so great, up to a hundred square miles for each pack, their numbers must have been considerable. It was in these conditions that they developed their social and hunting habits, which we shall look at.

This was a harsh, if prolific, habitat, and special qualities were demanded particularly of the predator species which occupied it. In addition to wolves and man, there were bobcats and lynxes, but they would be unable to secure prey except in rocky gullies and places where they could catch the animals by stealth. Only wolves and man could provide for their needs in the open snowy wastes. For

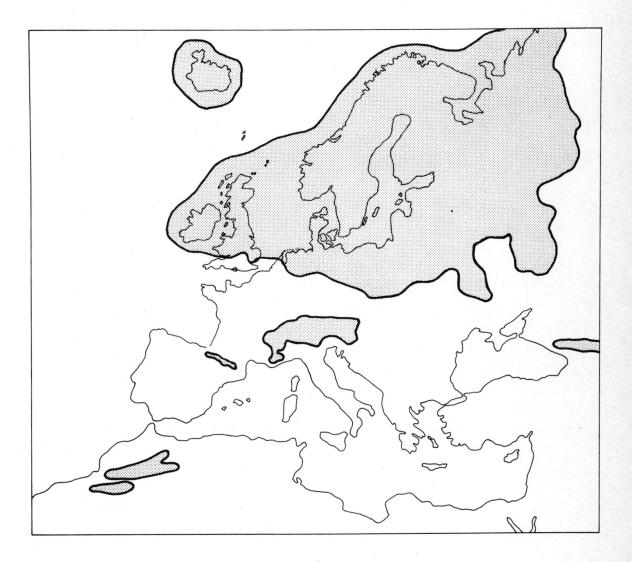

the wolves, this was their natural habitat and no special problems were posed. For man, on the other hand, problems were initially great, and evidence from fossil skeletons of the Neanderthaloids indicates that life was short and that man suffered from severe dietary deficiencies, particularly diseases of the bones arising from a shortage of vitamin D and of exposure to sunlight. Man had evidently migrated north from Africa, impelled either by the abundance of big game animals which he was able to hunt, or by population pressures in the well-watered North African plains; possibly both.

To the south of the tundras is the climatic formation of coniferous forest known as 'taiga'. This covers the sub-Arctic regions of the northern hemisphere. Today, the taiga is found far to the north in Scandinavia and northern Canada. During the Ice Ages, these forests were found far to the south and even extended to the Gulf of Mexico. The coniferous forests in the Mississippi Delta in southern Louisiana

are a surviving relic. Mammals that live in the taiga are moose and elk, and a number of species of deer. The taiga supports susliks, squirrels, marmots, chipmunks, and bears, which hibernate throughout the winter, unlike the true Arctic species. There are also beavers, rats, mice, lemmings, moles, shrews, and hares. Although today wolves are found in the taiga habitat and indeed follow the caribou migrating south into it, this is not their true homeland. Possibly, however, climatic conditions always did force those occupying the more southerly parts of the extended tundra to hunt in the taiga during the winter season. The natural predators of the taiga are such animals as weasels, polecats, wolverines, and other members of the Mustelidae.

When we attempt to visualise the conditions of life in the tundra/taiga habitat as it existed during the Ice Age, we can only go so far. The maps on pages 38 and 39 show the ice limits that exist today,

The musk ox, opposite, live in the very far north, where the wolves are large and tend to be white. These are tough opponents for the wolves, which do attack and eat them all the same.

The Arctic fox, a permanent tundra resident. It is one of the Canidae, like the wolf, but leads a different life. In the summer it shares the wolf's habitat without competition, living mainly on birds and eggs, and small rodents. It lacks the smell of many foxes, and some change the coat to white in winter.

41

and their southern limits at the height of the Ice Age. This vast area was the home of our ancestors, their home only some 600-700 generations ago. But for the great thaw that occurred between 20,000 and 10,000 years ago, it would still be our home. We would still be hunting the wild animals of this habitat in company with the wolves. Even in the Ice Age, this great expanse of land could hardly have been uniform. The great mountain ranges of the northern hemisphere existed then and, as today, the mountain vegetation resembled that of more northerly areas. There were glaciers near the equator, as shown by rock formations in south-west Uganda, just as today there is snow on the great African mountains, Ruwenzori and Kilimanjaro. Close to warm ocean currents the climate would be milder and the taiga would extend further north. Some areas would be sheltered by mountains, others would be exposed to the bitter Arctic winds where great plains existed. In the very far north, there was a great thickness and weight of ice on the land surfaces, as there is on the Antarctic today: in such areas, there was a desert of ice where no life existed. Even so, in the deep freeze below the ice there remained the seeds and spores of tundra plants, which remained viable and able to germinate after intervals even of thousands of years. Experiments with seeds taken from under glacier ice have shown this to be true.

Both preys of the wolf, the reindeer of northern Europe (top) and its close relative, the caribou of northern Canada and Alaska.

At the southern limits of the ice, a very small change in the annual mean temperature could cause a dramatic change of habitat in a comparatively short time. Dale Brown, in his fascinating book *Alaska*, quotes the instance of Glacier Bay, discovered in 1794 by the great British explorer, George Vancouver. At that date, the mouth of the bay was completely blocked by a great body of compact perpendicular ice, extending from shore to shore. The glacier had been on the advance for some 3,000 years and extended inland for 100 miles. By the end of the 19th century, one hundred years later, the glacier had receded 100 miles and the waters of the bay were ice-free. Today there is no ice anywhere in the bay or its many inlets. During this time, regeneration of the land through various stages has occurred to produce closed spruce forest, that is to say taiga. The spruce will in time be replaced by western hemlock. We tend to think of the ice cover as being something static. Even under conditions of today, when the ice cover is so far to the north, this is untrue; when the ice cover extended far to the south, variations during short climatic cycles must have been greatly magnified.

The areas over which wolves hunted must have been enormously variable, and we would expect their numbers to be greatly variable at the southern ice limits over comparatively short periods of time. That this happened is confirmed by the work of Russian scientists in

Wolf in the tundra conditions of Baffin Island.

the Caucasus, who have not only demonstrated this variation in numbers, but have also shown that there were in Pleistocene times races of large and small wolves. During the fiercest glaciation, the large predominated, but when the ice receded the smaller race became more numerous.

The physical topography of the land also determined the distribution of the great herds of grazing animals, and so also of their predators. In places, where there were narrow gaps between mountain ranges, the animals making their north/south migrations were forced to become concentrated to pass through the gaps. At such places, Palaeolithic man made his settlements, so as to waylay and trap the migrating animals. Huts made of mammoth tusks have been excavated at such points in Transylvania. Here too the wolves would be in evidence, feeding on man's leavings and hunting for themselves.

A factor influencing the type of vegetation in any area was the depth of the permafrost. Where the permanently frozen soil is only some six inches below the surface, only the poorest tundra vegetation can grow, with a high proportion of lichen and moss, the food of the reindeer and caribou. Where the permafrost is at a depth of some feet, then dwarf shrubs and trees such as alder and birch can take

Early man was quite unsuited to the Arctic habitat, and it was only his endurance and intelligence which helped him adapt to it.

root, the preferred food of the elk. In sheltered valleys, the depth of the permafrost is greater than in open plains.

It is indeed tantalising to speculate on the conditions of life to which our close ancestors were accustomed and with them their fellow predators, the wolves. We can only get an inkling of this by studying the surviving tundra in such places as Alaska and Greenland, bearing in mind that this does not represent the conditions that prevailed when tundra spread over so much of the northern hemisphere. We think of the tundra as bleak and inhospitable and we can be sure that most of us would not exchange it for our comfortable, well-warmed homes. Yet the tundra has a weird beauty in which travellers find a peculiar fascination. In the northerly tundra of today, the sun does not shine from November to February, though sunset and sunrise may be represented by a glow of twilight. Yet the scape is not dark. The many-coloured beams of the northern lights flash through the sky. The air is clear as crystal, and the moon shines brightly giving a white sheen to the snow; the stars twinkle in an unforgettable stardust. With the coming of spring, the ice and snow melt; the rivers flow and are alive with fish. The green plants hurriedly grow their leaves, so as to make the best use of the weak sun's rays. From May to August, there is perpetual daylight. The colours of the tundra vegetation are infinitely variable, changing with the

Present-day tundra, and the woodland taiga to its south. The tundra is the true home of the northern wolves, though they follow their prey into the taiga in winter.

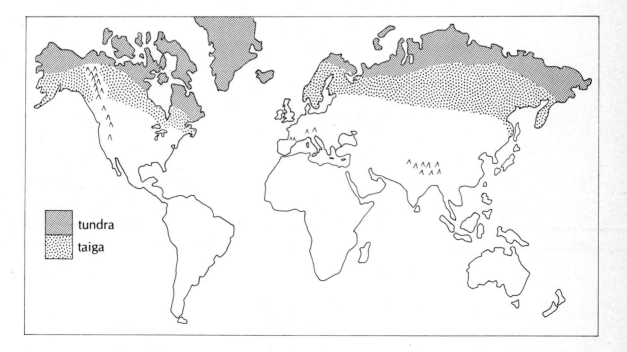

tundra
taiga

seasons. After the winter, the land is a grey/green, clothed with yellow, pink, blue, white and lavender flowers. In late August, it is russet, gold and red; by late September, all is brown dusted with white by the early snows. In autumn, there are numerous berries and fruits, which the tundra predators, both wolf and man, like to eat. At all times of the year when the tundra extended furthest south there was abundant food for both and life was good. It was only when the ice receded that difficulties arose; the habitat quickly became forested when the permafrost was melted, and there were hardships in finding a livelihood.

The preferred diet, indeed the staple diet, of the wolves, as of man, was the large grazing animals. But the habitat also provided an abundance of succulent small rodents, and fish and molluscs in plenty. In the more northerly areas wolves hunted the ungainly and dangerous musk ox, now greatly diminished in numbers. The typical prey animal of the tundra is the reindeer or caribou, seasonally

Creature of the borders of tundra and taiga, the elk, whose dangerous hooves and horns can injure predators; wolves will hesitate before attacking them.

46

migrating over great stretches of country and feeding on the lichen, the so-called reindeer moss. This lichen can grow where no other plants can survive, without roots and so independent of the depth of the permafrost. It is compounded of alga growing in commensalism with a fungus; the fungus absorbs water from the air, while the alga manufactures food material by photosynthesis and can fix atmospheric nitrogen. However, its rate of growth is immeasurably slow, and overgrazing will destroy it for hundreds of years, so the caribou must be perpetually on the move seeking new pastures. Twentieth-century attempts to pasture reindeer on this lichen have resulted in its total destruction.

Where taiga and tundra tend to merge, the great ungainly elk is found. In appearance, the elk is a caricature of an animal, with its long pendulous snout, great spreading horns more than six foot across, and its slender rump. It is, nevertheless, a formidable beast with dangerous hooves and horns that can do great damage to an

attacker. The elk is a browser and likes to feed on the foliage of small trees and shrubs. Wolves hesitate to attack him, unless very young or sick or injured. In mountainous areas are found the wild sheep (dall and bighorn) and goats, animals of great agility, capable of bounding away over the hill slopes and the boulders. Wolves are not at home in mountain habitats, and can rarely catch these agile creatures.

These are some of the creatures of the tundra on which wolves prey, each with its niche in the ecosystem, each demanding different skills to catch him. During the Ice Ages, there were many others spread over the great expanses of the tundra and in the hills and mountains. Nature with its great versatility found means to clothe

and populate the improbable bitterly cold habitat. The plants grow only to a low height, nestling down by the soil, where they are not only protected from the full blast of the icy winds, but also create a micro-climate many degrees warmer than the temperature even a few inches above the soil surface. Some plants, furthermore, are equipped with mechanisms to absorb and retain warmth inside hollow stems, so that their internal temperatures are relatively high. The many colourful flowering plants are fertilized by insects, and insect life in summer is abundant, including mosquitoes. The insects are preyed on particularly by the migrant birds which visit the Arctic regions during the summer. Though cold-blooded, the insects are protected

Sunshine and shadow in the interior of Alaska.

Opposite above, a herd of Norwegian reindeer, one of the main prey species of wolves in northern Europe. Below, grey wolves; howling is a group activity.

from the cold by a special physiological device: their body fluids contain glycerine which depresses their freezing point. The small mammals, such as rats, mice, voles, lemmings, and snowshoe hares, do not hibernate—the summer season is too short to permit them to accumulate enough reserves of fat to last through the nine months' winter season. The snow itself protects them; they burrow through it, feeding on deep-frozen roots, shoots and berries, protected by an insulating layer. They are preyed on by the wolverines, the Arctic foxes, and in certain seasons by the wolves. However, they breed prolifically and their population numbers are not diminished. Feeding partly on prey and partly on vegetable foods are the grizzly and brown bears. They also fish for salmon in the streams. They occupy rather different habitats from the wolves in ravines and more hilly areas. They are, nevertheless, not averse from finishing off an elk killed by the wolves. In the far north are the polar bears, which feed largely on seals and other marine foods. The seals and the polar bears are preyed on by Eskimos.

Barren tundra in winter. Large grazing animals cannot survive, although small rodents live under the snow on deep-frozen roots, seeds and nuts.

There is, then, abundant life in the tundra. Some of it, like the birds, the wolves, and the caribou, migrates with the change of season. The habitat cannot support dense populations, and the

growing season of plants is short. The number of species to be found is small compared with warmer parts of the earth. But for those that live there, life is rewarding and plentiful. It is strange that this unfriendly habitat should have fostered the two groups of animals, which are most highly organised in a social sense, which have greater powers of reasoning than most herbivores, and which in spite of their defects have developed a warmness of heart and sentiment outstanding in the animal kingdom. One may wonder at the strange paradox that these two groups, which hunt their prey and kill and devour them in merciless fashion, should have developed these particular properties, in response to a demanding habitat. One may even wonder why nature provides predators to cause suffering to prey species.

Why cannot the unfortunate animals, which demand no more than to live on the vegetation, be left in peace to do so? Why is it the predators which become intelligent, more able to reason, and endowed with higher faculties? The herbivore, with its enormous, bulky apparatus for the digestion of cellulose and fibre, must spend a great part of the day's twenty-four hours in acquiring and digesting food. Even so, this is only achieved with the aid of innumerable

Opposite, the varied landscape of the taiga.

The taiga is the home of valuable fur-bearing animals hunted by men with an irrational fear of wolves, and who lose no opportunity of persecuting them.

micro-organisms which ferment the vegetable foods in the capacious organs of digestion. It follows that higher pursuits, as indulged in by man and which permit the social interplay in which wolves indulge, essentially require a more concentrated form of food which only predation can supply.

It is often said that predation is a waste of nature's resources. At each step in the food chain, as much as 20 per cent of the energy initially acquired by plants through photosynthesis is lost. This argument takes no account of one significant point: at each step, energy and the building materials for the body become available in a more concentrated form, and so they can be acquired more efficiently by the next predator in the chain. Very recent research by Michael

Compare the wolf with the bear, a lumbering and slow-moving creature more like the ancestral carnivores, quite unable to pursue and hunt down prey. They are both tundra predators, the bear more accustomed to canyons and gullies.

Coyotes, a group of Canidae which can in effect be considered as wolves, do not arouse the same hostility, and are found in some areas from which true wolves have disappeared.

Crawford at the Nuffield Institute of Comparative Medicine in London tends to indicate that the unsaturated fats of the nervous tissues of the kind that make up the brain of a sophisticated predator, such as the wolf, could not be constructed within the normal growing period purely from products of plant material. It is necessary that these materials be first built into the tissues of a herbivorous animal, so that the predator needs fewer steps to organise them further.

The tundra habitat, from its cruel environment, has produced great beauty of scenery, great and lovely contrasts, and a bountiful living for many interesting creatures. It has also produced the two most versatile predators that the world has known, wolf and man, both equipped with higher intellectual faculties than had been previously achieved in evolutionary times. The wolf was evolved in the tundra; man was an intruder and could not have survived there without his special intellectual qualities. The great extent of the tundra was destroyed by climatic change, not by man. The wolf would, in time, have conformed to the new situation. Not so man, who failed to appreciate the environment developed after the Ice Age, and set out to make it conform to his will. It was the intellectual capacity he developed in the Arctic climate that enabled him to do so. In this sense, the tundra is the true cradle of civilisation.

Ecology and population

The tundra habitat could never support large populations of animals, and animals which live there must be perpetually on the move. The regulation of population numbers is essential if the habitat is not to be destroyed. In a peculiar way, nature's methods of population control affect of themselves the character of the animals, as we shall now see.

The first principles of ecology state that the life forms which occupy a habitat must be adjusted to it. Where this is achieved, the habitat is improved and its carrying capacity is increased. If the adjustment is disturbed, the habitat deteriorates and its carrying capacity declines. This adjustment has been achieved for the world's major habitats during aeons of evolution, and a number of mechanisms for controlling animal numbers have come into being which ensure long-term stability. Of all God's creatures, only man has attempted to make himself independent of ecological rules by artificially altering habitats to suit his needs, and thereby multiplying more than the unaltered habitat could justify. In so doing he has destroyed a great many habitats, though life has been improved in others.

Wolves, however, are no exception to nature's laws; their numbers must be limited to what their territories can provide and to the food available to them during their seasonal migrations. The numbers of human populations were similarly controlled until the end of the Ice Age, when man too lived in nomadic bands, and his numbers conformed to the food materials available to him by hunting and gleaning. To understand the wolf, therefore, it is necessary to discuss those mechanisms which control population numbers, and see what part they have played in determining his nature and character.

A Canadian timber wolf about to adopt a submissive posture—the hierarchical social organisation of wolves may be linked with the control of population by the effects of stress.

57

Basically, the carrying capacity of a habitat is determined by two major factors only, namely the climate and the condition of the soil. These two factors determine the nature and amount of the vegetation. This in turn determines the amount of food available for the production of animals that live on it, the primary producers as they are called, and their numbers determine the numbers of predators that can be supported by preying on them.

Predators may be first-stage, second-stage or even third-stage. For example, the primary producer may be a small rodent, living on nuts and roots; the second stage may be a fox, which eats the rodent; the fox may be eaten by a wolf, who thus constitutes the third stage. Alternatively, a bird may eat insects which live on plant produce and are thus the first stage; the bird's eggs may be eaten by a rat, the second stage; the rat may be eaten by a marten, the third stage; and the marten may be eaten by a wolf, the fourth stage. Again, the food chain may lead from insect larvae, by way of a minnow to a trout, to a bird, and so by way of a fox to a wolf. Since at each stage as much as 20 per cent of the energy originally acquired from the light rays of the sun (the photons) is lost in waste, the greater the number of stages the less energy is available to the final predator and so the smaller the numbers that the habitat can support.

The less prolific the habitat, the simpler is the food chain. In the tropics, where the light intensity is high, food chains are very complex. In desert and Arctic areas, food chains are more simple and the numbers of species supported are comparatively small. Wolves are basically first-stage predators, since they prey on the primary producers—the great grazing animals. They also prey on rodents and hares, which are also primary producers. In a sense, they are also primary producers themselves, because at certain times of the year they eat fruits and berries. They are only second- or third-stage predators when they eat birds, fish and such animals as foxes.

One would expect, therefore, that wolves would obtain maximum permissible densities in habitats that are suitable to them, such as the tundra and grassy plains. This density is not high, as we have seen, since a wolf pack may require as much as 100 square miles to support it. But, paradoxically, higher densities are found in habitats that are not suitable for them, such as forest and mountain; in such areas they are driven to raid flocks and herds outside the habitat and their way of life is perforce altered. Even in their preferred habitat conditions may change rapidly, and such changes have an effect on the abundance of prey species. A worsening of the climate may lead to a reduction in the fodder available to the grazers. When numbers of prey animals become reduced, initially there follows an increase in the numbers of predators and scavengers, because there are more

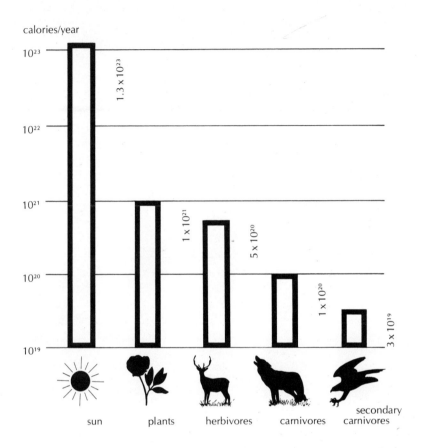

calories/year

10^{23}

1.3×10^{23}

10^{22}

10^{21}

1×10^{21}

5×10^{20}

10^{20}

1×10^{20}

3×10^{19}

10^{19}

sun   plants   herbivores   carnivores   secondary carnivores

Utilization of solar energy decreases with each step along the food chain. Plants use only 0.08 of the energy reaching the atmosphere; plant-eaters use only a fraction of this, and carnivores less still.

weak and sick animals available to be caught and so food is more plentiful. The numbers of predators, therefore, become initially increased, but subsequently there are too many for the available food and numbers must be drastically reduced. A further mechanism operates to increase the numbers of predators at certain times. Many small animals, such as lemmings and snowshoe hares, show regular fluctuations of population numbers which are independent of climatic cycles. The lemmings, for example, come to a population peak or 'explosion' cyclically every four years, following which there is a population 'crash'. At times of population explosion, the numbers of their first-stage predators also rise to a peak, and so they too must decline when the crash occurs.

For whatever reason, wolves do at times become too numerous. At such times, they are observed to be thin and weak, and lacking in stamina. More than this, they suffer from active ill-health as a result of acute and chronic diseases, which infect them. Normally, wolves are very healthy animals and are rarely seen to be sick. They support

A Canadian timber wolf in a natural, alert posture.

a certain number of fleas, which seem to breed in their dens. They carry—as do all wild animals—roundworms and tapeworms, but apart from this they do not suffer from any ailments that have been described. However, at times of population excess they suffer severely from two major epidemic diseases, namely rabies and distemper, and a great many die. Rabies is endemic in tundra habitats, such as Alaska, though in normal circumstances it appears to be only rarely contracted by the wolves. What animals constitute the reservoir of the disease cannot be said. Presumably, though, the wolves in times of stress attack small predatory animals they would otherwise ignore, are bitten and become rabid. Rabid wolves, as we have seen, develop abnormal behaviour patterns and attack human beings. It is also difficult to see where distemper originates. Possibly it is endemic in wolf populations, but only becomes severe when they are in a weakened condition. Whatever the reason, whenever the wolf populations become excessive, disease takes a toll and thereby tends to reduce them. However, nature has more fundamental means of reducing excess populations which operate in all wild animals, even the most primitive. This is known as 'stress'.

The so-called 'stress' state is a very important population-controlling mechanism in all groups of wild animals, though it may operate somewhat differently in some than in others. The condition has been investigated by ecologists in many different groups of animals though the author does not know any studies made of stress in wolves. The same conditions have been independently studied as an element of pathology and disease by the well-known Canadian physiologist, Hans Selye. As a result, a good deal is known of this strange mechanism, but it is still not fully understood. Stress is a state which is induced by any kind of trauma. This can be malnutrition, injury, disease, or psychological disturbance. There are three stages to the condition: the stage of alarm, the stage of resistance, and the stage of exhaustion. During its course, there is an increased demand for the so-called cortico-steroids, hormones from the outer portion of the adrenal glands. If the demand is sudden and the gland is unable to cope with it, immediate death occurs as in death from fright; this is the first stage. If the animal survives the first stage, the adrenal gland becomes much enlarged and so increases the hormone output; this is the stage of compensation. If, however, a second stress is imposed on the first, or if the original stress is intensified, there occurs the stage of exhaustion, and this leads to death also. An animal in the second stage of stress suffers from a number of physiological changes which influence its behaviour and other important bodily mechanisms. A stressed animal is quarrelsome and inclined to fight. Its resistance to disease is lowered, and its blood pressure, blood-clotting and other mechanisms are disturbed.

Rolling in odorous substance is a behavioural trait found both in wolves and domesticated dogs. The snow is marked with urine often to indicate the edge of a territory.

Now, the function of the adrenal gland is regulated by another endocrine gland, the pituitary gland situated at the base of the brain. This gland is in close association with nerve fibres coming from the brain by which its function is regulated, so that any psychological disturbance is readily transmitted to it from the higher centres of nervous activity. At times of stress, messages are sent to the pituitary gland to arrange for a greater output of adrenal hormones, and in this way the animal is prepared to meet the stress. This is done at the expense of hormones going to the sex glands, so that their activity is diminished. The effect is threefold—pregnant females are inclined to abort their foetuses, the urge to mate is reduced (reduction of 'fecundity'), and if mating occurs, pregnancy less readily takes place, or the numbers of fertilised ova are reduced (reduction of 'fertility)'. In wolves, it has been observed that at times of population pressure fewer cubs are born in a litter.

The stressed state is also linked with the hierarchy system. It has been found in some groups of animals, though not so far in wolves, that the subordinate members of the hierarchy always have enlarged adrenal glands, that is they are in a permanently stressed state. When the herd or pack itself enters a state of stress, such animals receive a double stressing dose which could lead to the third stage and then to their deaths. Alternatively, the young subordinate males especially— but sometimes the females also—may be driven from the territory to fend for themselves. Such treatment will usually lead to their deaths at the hands of predators or from the owners of neighbouring territories. Since in their stressed state they are the first to contract infectious diseases, they serve to spread the infection and thus create epidemics. The stress mechanism in this way serves to preserve the stronger members of the pack, while eliminating the weaker.

Researches on stress, in which mice are usually used, have shown that the stress response can be caused by population pressures alone, and not by a shortage of food. When a mouse colony is started, the mice rapidly increase in numbers until a certain density is reached. The breeding rate is then automatically diminished as the animals become stressed. There is much quarrelling and fighting and newborn litters of baby mice are killed and eaten. This occurs even though sufficient food is supplied for all the mice in the colony. It therefore follows that the stressed state occurs solely because of population density and not because of a shortage of food.

These strange responses to problems of population serve to explain how it is that wolves adjust their numbers so accurately to the resources of their habitat. Their social instincts are so highly developed that the hierarchy system is especially strong, and the position of the dominant members of the pack is rarely challenged until they become too old. The subordinates accept their position, in addition to which there is usually an 'outcast' member of the pack, who keeps away from the other wolves and only feeds on sufferance on their leavings. Furthermore, no wolves, male or female, will mate until they have acquired a territory, so that normally all cubs born are potential heirs to a property on which they in their turn can raise their families. In most animal species, the numbers of young born are in proportion to their expectancy of survival. A female tick, for example, lays millions of eggs which hatch into larvae. The larvae can only survive and grow into adult ticks if by chance their host animal brushes past so that they can cling to it. The chance of this is very small, so that the great numbers of larvae are essential for race survival. The same is true of any blood parasites that the tick may carry. Small birds, in which there is a high mortality of the chicks, lay larger clutches of eggs than larger birds, whose young are less vulnerable. The general rule is that more young are produced than are expected to survive. There is thus always a surplus to allow for wastage. In wolves, which have a breeding life of seven or eight years, litters of even one would be more than enough to maintain population numbers. Their large litters of seven or eight allow for considerable wastage, for expansion into new territories when climatic conditions are favourable, and for re-establishment of the former population after unfavourable periods. This is the reason why attempts to control wolf numbers have been so unsuccessful in the past, except where their breeding habitats have been destroyed.

There is no evidence that wolf numbers fluctuate cyclically as with lemmings and snowshoe hares. Indeed, what evidence there is tends to show that they do not. Provided that food is ample, their numbers are maintained in relation to the numbers of territories available. So resourceful are they that for a time at any rate they can find alternative foods to provide their needs. In order to survive, wolves will consume a variety of unnatural foods, carrion, insects, molluscs, and vegetable materials. There is little precise information on the subject relating to wolves, but it is noteworthy that, following the rapid elimination of rabbits through myxomatosis, the numbers of foxes in Britain, contrary to expectation, did not markedly diminish. They somehow found other things to eat, and their raids on domestic poultry and turkeys increased for a time.

The effect of domestication seems to diminish the operation of the stress mechanism. Man, regarded as a domesticated animal, habitually breeds regardless of the effect this will have on his habitat, of the availability of territory, or the adequacy of food resources. He crowds himself in tightly packed urban populations, seemingly without regard to the density achieved. The result is that lives are led in insanitary conditions, and the expectation of life is correspondingly reduced. With many truly primitive peoples living in pre-agricultural conditions, such as the Kalahari Bushmen, this does not happen. The numbers of young born, without benefit of the 'pill' and other contraceptive devices, are adequate to maintain the population and no more. The same is true of domestic dogs, whose population numbers are regulated by their masters. Dogs often suffer the most terrible injuries without showing signs of shock or stress. Indeed, a dog may lose a leg from being hit by a car and run to its master wagging its tail to show how pleased it is to see him. He only shows stress, even to the extent of dying from it, when his master neglects him, leaves him, or dies.

At the borders of any habitat favourable to a particular life form, there is always a 'tension zone' where different habitats merge. These form the outer limits, where the 'ecotypes' change, but there is inevitably some overlap where the species from the one habitat compete with those from the other. The fringes of the two habitats may indeed shift seasonally or periodically in ways that have already been discussed. In such areas, species tend to change their ways of life to compete with the demands of the shifting habitat boundaries. Wolves are so resilient, and can survive on such a wide variety of foods, that when their way of life has been threatened they adapt themselves to altered conditions with an unusual degree of success. At the end of the Ice Age wolves survived in forested and mountainous areas in the face of persecution by man. The forests replaced the tundra with such great rapidity—a matter of a few hundred years—that no other large predator emerged to challenge his dominance.

Had the wolf's position not been challenged by man, presumably a form of forest wolf would have developed by natural selection as a sub-species, just as the Tibetan and Japanese wolves became adapted to mountainous habitats. If it is correct to regard the northern grey wolves of the tundra as the ancestral form from which other sub-species and species were evolved, then this sort of process has happened before.

The southerly spread of wolves which took place in the Pleistocene, whether at the time of the glaciations or during their intermissions, reveals the capacity of wolves to colonise new habitats, develop new characters and thus become adapted to them. In North America, the northern grey wolves (*Canis lupus*) merge—or did merge until they were nearly extinguished—into the red wolves (*Canis rufus*), rather smaller than the type species and showing great variations of colouration. Further south, an even more unusual form of wolf is found in the maned wolves (*Canis jubatus*) which are in fact forest wolves and no longer hunt in packs. Further south still were the wolves of Tierra del Fuego, *Canis lupus magellanicus*, and those of the Falkland Islands, *Canis lupus antarcticus*, less dissimilar from the type species than are the maned wolves.

In Asia, we find south of the range of the northern wolves the Asian pale-footed wolves, *Canis lupus pallipes*. They are much smaller than the northern wolves and differ in their colouration, and in their habits and ways of life. However, here again we have an offshoot of the ancestral stock which has become adapted with great success to a new way of life and to a different kind of habitat. The Asian wolves again at the edge of their habitat merge into another sub-species of wolf, the Arabian wolf, *Canis lupus arabs*, which is adapted to life in desert country; these two have developed special properties, which adapt them to the terrain in which they live. It is indeed a far cry from tundra to desert, though both are suited to wolves in being open.

It is known from Ancient Egyptian records that wolves at one time existed in Egypt and the Western Desert. In those days, much of the Sahara supported savannah vegetation and nomadic peoples lived there with their herds and hunted gazelle and other wild animals. It is tantalising that we do not know what those wolves were like. Were they the Arabian wolves or the pale-footed Asian wolves or some distinct species?

Further south in Africa, we find the Cape hunting dogs, classified because of a tooth variation and different digit numbers as *Lycaon pictus*, and not as wolves. However, their pack-hunting and other habits closely resemble those of true wolves although their evolutionary background is somewhat different. These animals are distributed as far south as the Cape. They are acclimatised to the African climate and their ways of life are adapted to hunting in savannah conditions.

These migrations and adaptations of canid stock have occurred entirely during the Pleistocene epoch, within the past 100,000 years. They illustrate the great genetic potentiality of the wolf and his relatives. Except for man and small animals such as rats and mice, no other mammal has shown such adaptability. One reason may be that only on open terrain such as the tundra was a predator evolved which could, by social organisation, learn to attack large prey in open spaces. It was only in these areas, in turn, that there appeared an animal of sufficient intelligence to exploit the opportunities offered by so many different habitats.

Wolves and their relations

Dogs, jackals, wolves, foxes, and a number of so-called wild dogs all belong to the Family Canidae, Order Carnivora, Class Mammalia. Other Carnivora include the Ursidae (the bear family), the Mustelidae (stoats, weasels, and otters), the Procyonidae (raccoons), the Ailuridae (pandas), the Viverridae (genets and civets) and the Felidae (cats). The Order Carnivora originated in the Tertiary period as a primitive group of mammals, given the generic name of *Amphictis*. *Amphictis* was a small unspecialised, carnivorous animal which moved rather slowly, walking on its palms and soles; it lived and reared its young in burrows and it was able to revert to other forms of food if prey was difficult to find. These animals were not able to defend themselves very well, and their young were born in a very helpless condition, as are those of this group of Carnivora today. They would have had little future without becoming further specialised through natural selection, which produced more efficient types. They lived some twelve million years ago, when the Miocene period was verging into the Pliocene.

It is believed that the bears and dog family were derived from a single root, and the Swedish zoologist Winge in his book *Relationships of the Mammalian Genera*, published in 1941, gives a classification of the bear family Ursidae making Canini a sub-group of that family.

On the face of it, these two groups are so dissimilar that such a close relationship seems improbable. However, Winge's conclusions have some support ecologically as well as anatomically. Both bears and wolves live in very similar habitats, though they occupy different regions in them. For example, the Russians say that in the tundra zones, where you find bears, wolves are absent, and vice versa. Supposedly, therefore, each group became adapted to different niches in the same areas, thus dividing up the hunting territories between them. The common ancestor was a primitive form of ursid known as *Cynodictis*. This animal's body resembled the most primitive

The northern wolf. Compare him with the dingo, and the other Canidae in this chapter. He is the child of the Ice Age and can sleep in the open in the coldest winters.

67

forms of the Viverridae (civets and genets), with rather short limbs, five fingers and five toes. It is easy to see how from such an animal there could be evolved on the one hand a large blundering beast like the bear, and on the other hand by lengthening of the limb and development of powers of rapid movement and stamina another group such as the Canidae. A further offshoot of the same stem were the Mustelidae, the stoats, polecats, weasels, wolverines, skunks, badgers and otters. This group had an evident liking for water, thus filling a third niche, and an offshoot of them are the seals, sea-lions, and walruses.

At some stage, there must have existed a common ancestral type of the Canidae from which all other diverse forms have evolved. It seems most likely that this was a form resembling mostly the northern grey wolves, and that the Family Canidae first appeared in northern regions, such as those inhabited by the northern wolves today. From their ancestral lands the Canidae have spread virtually throughout the world, with the exception of New Zealand and some Polynesian islands. In Australia, the group is represented by the dingos, *Canis familiaris dingo*, semi-domesticated wolves or dogs undoubtedly introduced by the Aborigines during the late stages of the last Ice Age. In the New World, canid forms were formerly found from the Falkland Islands and the Straits of Magellan to the icy wastes of the very far north. Various forms were present through-out the whole of Europe and Asia and the whole of Africa. Though appearing on the scene so late they were among the most successful of all groups of animals; the true wolves apart, they still exist in most of these areas as jackals, foxes, or wild dogs.

Dingo dogs resemble the Asian group of wolves so closely as to leave no doubt of direct descent from them.

This is not the place for a detailed classification of the Canidae, a complicated subject on which taxonomists hold a variety of opinions. In fact there has been no really comprehensive and authoritative monograph on them since Mivart's, published in 1890, and further developed by Winge in 1940. In the brief survey of the wolf's relatives that follows in this chapter, Mivart's classification has been generally followed, as it seems to the author to be still the most reliable in many ways. But classification of the Canidae is still an open question among specialists, and it is worth looking in passing at the sort of problem that arises.

Mivart, supported later by Winge, placed foxes in the genus *Canis*; other taxonomists, however, have generally invented further, separate, genera for foxes. For example, the late R. I. Pocock, an acknowledged expert on Canidae, recognised red foxes as *Vulpes vulpes*, Bengal foxes as *V. bengalensis*, fennecs as *V. zerda*, and Arctic foxes as *Alopex lagopus*. Maurice Burton in 1962, on the other hand, classed fennecs as *Fennecus zerda*.

The features given by Pocock as distinguishing fox genera from *Canis* were: 'the pads of the feet being more hairy, and the tail *usually* [author's italics] longer and hairier and by the *very slight* [author's italics] development of air cells in the bones of the forehead.' Pocock goes on to say that the Arctic fox in some respects approaches the wolves and the jackals. But the characters which separate the genera *Vulpes*, *Alopex* and *Fennecus* from *Canis* seem to the present author to be so insubstantial that the classification of Mivart and Winge is preferable, based as it is on definite and easily recognisable features.

All Canidae resemble either the common wolf or the common fox, though they vary a good deal in size, and some may dispute the likeness in the case of some South American wild dogs. In different groups the legs may be longer or shorter; tails may be shorter than the wolf's, though never longer than the fox's brush; the ears are sometimes very large but are always erect except in some breeds of domestic dogs and in puppies. The colouration of wild species varies from grey to yellowish or reddish brown, though some Arctic species are white, and black varieties are not uncommon; the back, upper surface of the head and some parts of the limbs are generally darker than the flanks; the underparts are always paler or even white; the tips and inner parts of the ears may be white, though the external surfaces are coloured.

As with many other characteristics, the colouration is variable within a single species. The coat may be longer in winter and lighter in colour or even white. Only in bush dogs is the tail really short, and only in the fennec foxes and the bat-eared foxes are the ears excessively long; even in these species the ears do not droop as in some domestic dogs. In wild Canidae, the length and quality of the fur are variable. There is no big toe (hallux) on the hind feet, although a residual fifth toe is often present in domestic dogs in the form of dew claws. In true dogs (*Canis*), a short thumb (pollex) is present on the front feet though it does not reach the ground. It does not appear in the Cape hunting dogs (*Lycaon*), but is concealed beneath the skin. In no Canidae can the claws be retracted.

In all Canidae, anatomical features are so alike as to make them virtually indistinguishable. Indeed, it is very difficult to classify them into genera. This is done primarily by means of slightly differing tooth formulae. The tooth formula of dogs is, in each side of the jaw: incisors 3; canines 1; premolars 4; molars 2 above and 3 below. This is expressed:

$$I\frac{3}{3} \quad C\frac{1}{1} \quad P\frac{4}{4} \quad M\frac{2}{3} = \frac{10}{11}$$

Renard the fox, in some ways the most successful and widespread of the Canidae, is in fact not as sagacious as the wolf, but his habits do not arouse the same suspicion as the wolf's.

One true molar, that is a tooth not preceded by a milk tooth, is present in all genera in the upper jaw, and there are at least two in the lower. The bush dogs have only this number of molars. In bat-eared foxes the molars are more or less uniform; however in other

Canidae the fourth premolar in the upper jaw and the first molar in the lower jaw form the great tearing carnassial teeth, which in the northern wolf exceed in width the combined length of the two preceding teeth. Mivart's classification of the Canidae, based mainly on tooth formulae, is shown here:

$$
\text{Digits } 5\text{–}4
\begin{cases}
M\,\tfrac{1}{2} & \textit{Icticyon (Speothos)} \\[1.2em]
M\,\tfrac{2}{3} & \textit{Canis} \\[1.2em]
M\,\tfrac{2}{2} & \textit{Cuon} \\[1.2em]
M\,\tfrac{3}{4} & \textit{Otocyon}
\end{cases}
$$

Digits 4–4   *Lycaon*

Canidae are remarkably uniform in their way of life and organisation. All make greater or lesser use of burrows. Sometimes these are simple, but sometimes they are so extensive as to constitute an underground canine village. The extent to which burrows are made for living in or merely for giving birth and raising the puppies depends largely on habitat. Foxes living in moist forested countries, frequently hunted and persecuted, make extensive burrows for warmth and security, and also because the soil is suitable for this kind of activity. In desert countries, where burrowing may be difficult, jackals, coyotes, and desert foxes will find themselves secure resting places among boulders, where they can lie up and bear their young. All genera find some kind of burrow or nest in which to give birth; all produce litters of from 3 to 12 puppies, which are born helpless and blind after a gestation period of 62 to 68 days.

Various species, such as the wolves, hunt their prey in packs, while other species, although closely related, have forgone this type of life. The red wolf of Texas will combine in packs particularly in winter and is a source of danger to herds of cattle. The maned wolf of South America, on the other hand, lives in solitary state and attacks only small game. Other Canidae, such as jackals, live mainly on carrion, young birds and eggs; they will also eat lizards, mice, snails, and insects such as white ants and moths. They also occasionally combine in packs to hunt live animals. Other species of wild dogs living along rivers or by the sea will eat crustaceans and molluscs. The grey northern wolves also eat fish. Some species of Canidae eat vegetable foods and fruit, and indeed the northern wolves during the autumn commonly eat certain berries which are in season and of

Maned wolves are found only in forested parts of South America. Thought to be derived from the more northerly red wolves, they do not combine in packs to hunt. Note the long legs, and the appearance otherwise like a red fox.

which they are very fond. It is well-known in Britain that the common fox eats an enormously varied diet. At one time it relied largely on rabbits, but when these were no longer available because of myxomatosis, the numbers of foxes did not diminish; they found alternative forms of food, although admittedly they made more frequent raids on poultry and turkey farms. Apart from this they found sustenance by eating invertebrates, roots, carrion and anything else they could find. The group of small wolves, the coyotes (*Canis latrans*), have taken to scavenging, like jackals in European and Asian countries. Jackals are known as the great scavengers of southern European and eastern countries. However, true wolves in time of scarcity will also scavenge, though they do not generally like feeding on carrion, while at times jackals will combine into a pack to go hunting.

It would appear, on the face of it, that foxes are dissimilar from other members of the Canidae—they are solitary hunters and never combine into packs. They have an age-old and probably well-justified reputation for sagacity and cunning. Foxes also show varying features in their different species and habitats. The common red fox for example has a characteristic and rather unpleasant odour. The Arctic foxes have no such odour.

If further evidence of the common identity of the various species of the genus *Canis* is sought, all, with the possible exception of the foxes, readily interbreed and produce fertile offspring. The question of hybridization between dogs and foxes is hotly disputed. Some say that hybrids do occur, but this is denied by others and there appear to be no authentic records of such hybrids between either domestic dogs or wolves on the one hand and foxes on the other. In her monograph on mammalian hybrids (1954) Annie P. Gray writes:

> Presumed hybrids have been reported from time to time between domestic dog and red fox, but most observers agree that hybridization between the dog and the fox does not take place, even in captivity. The two species have, exceptionally, shown sexual interest in each other, but copulation has not been observed, except possibly by Niemeyer. Clement and Kriznecky report that a fox terrier bitch inseminated with fox semen showed a swelling of the mammary glands and colostrum secretion 65 days after insemination, but abdominal palpation revealed no foetus. Seventy-one days after artificial insemination, pressure on the mammary gland produced milk. A week later all symptoms of pregnancy had disappeared. It is suggested that the foetus died and was aborted.

However, this same author reports a non-fertile cross between a female pampas fox reared with a mongrel fox terrier; two litters were produced comprising a single pup, then four pups; only the single pup survived. There are, however, differences of chromosome numbers between dogs including wolves, foxes, and jackals, so that speciation is evidently in progress.

The wild Canidae fall into eight different groups, although the relationships between them are by no means clear, as we will see. The groups are: 1 the true wolves, 2 the jackals, 3 the wild dogs, 4 the foxes, 5 the dholes, 6 the bush dogs, 7 the hyaena dog or Cape hunting dog, and 8 the large-eared Cape dog or fox.

Lions hunt by stealth, not in packs. This one, and its prey, are being surveyed by a jackal hoping to share in the spoils.

The true wolves

There are six varieties of true wolf classified as *Canis lupus*: *Canis lupus* (the type species), *Canis lupus pallipes* (the Asian wolves), *Canis lupus chanco* (the Tibetan wolves), *Canis lupus arabs* (the Arabian desert wolf), *Canis lupus hodophylax* (Japanese wolves), and *Canis lupus antarcticus* (the Antarctic wolves). Closely allied to them are: *Canis rufus* (the red wolves of Texas), *Canis jubatus* (the maned wolves of South America), *Canis latrans* (the prairie wolves or coyotes), and *Canis simenesis* (the Abyssinian wolves). The northern grey wolves, the Asian wolves, the Tibetan wolves, the Japanese wolves and the Antarctic wolves are very similar to each other, though varying somewhat in size, colouration, and conformation. The Japanese wolves have become extinct during the past thirty years, and the Antarctic wolves found formerly only in the Falkland Islands are also extinct. The northern grey wolves, which form mostly the subject of this book, are greatly diminished in numbers, but still occupy a considerable terrain in the Arctic Circle. The red wolves of Texas, which occupy a habitat to the south of the grey wolves, are nearly extinct, though there are a few survivors in Texas and Louisiana. It is said, however, that they have taken to hybridizing with the coyotes and that the hybrid form is holding its own. This is believed to be because the true wolves are reluctant to take carrion, whereas the coyotes have become scavengers like jackals and are

Coyotes are in reality small wolves, and similar to true wolves in appearance and behaviour, although they have taken secondarily to scavenging and are more willing to consume carrion.

The Canadian timber wolf.

Red wolves once occupied a habitat south of the grey wolves, extending down across the U.S. into Mexico. They are smaller than them in size, though larger than the coyotes.

Lobo, a Canadian timber wolf brought into captivity. The grey wolves vary greatly in character—if taken as cubs many adapt readily to a captive way of life

therefore persecuted to a lesser extent than the true wolves; however, no doubt the greater size of the wolves gives some advantage to the crossed progeny.

The pale-footed Asian wolves are confined to the plains south of the Himalayas, and behave as do true wolves, hunting in packs to acquire their prey. They were formerly widely distributed from India to Palestine, and have in recent times reappeared in some of their former habitats in Palestine and Syria. They are smaller and slighter than the northern wolves and have shorter coats with little or no under-fur. Unlike the northern wolves they have in India developed undesirable characters and a large number of children used to be carried off every year, giving rise to stories of male infants being suckled and reared by wolves, stories which are of doubtful authenticity. The Asian wolves are of great importance, because they are certainly the ancestors of one of the great groups of domestic dogs, the dingos, which are almost indistinguishable from them except for their smaller size and yellowish colour. The problems of dog ancestry will be discussed in a later chapter. The other wolves implicated are the northern grey wolves, the Tibetan wolves and the Arabian desert wolves.

The true wolves then are all variations on a single theme, differing according to their habitat and way of life. Even the northern wolves have been sub-divided by many workers into numerous varieties all differing slightly in size and colour, though very uniform in their habits. The next group of wild dogs to be considered, the jackals, are very similar to the true wolves, though their habit of scavenging has brought differences of temperament if not of anatomy.

The jackals

Jackals have no distinctive anatomical features which separate them from wolves or domestic dogs. The parietal crest, the ridge of bone which runs along the cranium and to which the great muscles of mastication are attached, though always present in wolves, may sometimes be absent in jackals as it sometimes is in domestic dogs. The jackals lack the savage defensive powers of the true wolves and are much more timid; they are often preyed on by other predators such as leopards. They breed in burrows, which are usually more extensive than those of wolves and produce four pups in a litter. They will inter-breed freely with domestic dogs and produce fertile offspring. However, as we have already seen, jackals will sometimes combine in packs and pull down quite large animals and they often give tongue in wolf-like howls. There are three species of jackal: the golden jackal, the black-backed jackal, and the side-striped jackal. The golden jackals are found in Greece and Turkey as far west as

Jackals are closely related to wolves, and undoubtedly descended from them. They are similar anatomically but have different, less powerful and aggressive temperaments. This is a black-backed jackal.

Two side-striped jackals. Jackals will, under pressure, sometimes revert to wolf type by combining in packs to hunt.

Dalmatia, in the Caucasus and Asia Minor, and eastwards through India. The other two species are all African. The black-backed jackals are widely spread over southern Africa, and are also found in Ethiopia. The side-striped jackals are found in limited areas of East Africa.

The wild dogs

There are six species of Canidae whose exact position within the group is not too well understood, and which are referred to commonly as wild dogs. These are to be found in South America. The first species, Magellanic dog or colpeo, is similar to the Falkland Island wolf described earlier. These dogs are found in a wide variety of terrain from the humid forests of Tierra del Fuego to the almost desert country of northern Chile, extending along the western coast of South America for some 1,600 miles. They live mainly in woods, but are chiefly nocturnal and are seldom seen by day. The carasissi or crab-eating dog ranges through the forests and bushy plains of South America from the Orinoco to La Plata, but does not extend into the pampas region. Crab-eating dogs are commonly spoken of as foxes, to which they bear some resemblance. They prey on small animals like agoutis and pacas, and on birds; sometimes they will combine in packs and run down deer. They have their name because they frequently catch and eat crayfish in the rivers. The small-eared dog is found in Amazonia. It stands about fourteen inches high and frequents the banks of rivers. The nose is elongated and pointed, the ears very short and the fur also short and generally of a dark-grey colour. Little is known about its habits. Azara's dog is found over the greater part of South America east of the Andes, but does occur on both sides of the mountain chain. It inhabits bushy regions from which it makes excursions into the great forest on the one side and into the open country on the other. It seeks its prey at twilight and at night, feeding on small quadrupeds and birds. It will also eat frogs and lizards and it bites through and sucks sugar cane on the plantations causing a great deal of damage and waste. These dogs readily fraternise with domestic dogs, and will hunt in packs with them. They are also easily tamed, when the puppies are taken young. They know their own master and are friendly with him, but are not very obedient unless a stick is used, and they have a disagreeable odour like foxes. The small-toothed dog and the stripe-tailed dog are both Brazilian forms, which bear some resemblance to each other. They are remarkable for the structure of their carnassial teeth which are not very typical of Canidae, and their exact position in the group is not clear.

The true foxes

The foxes show as much variability as do the wolves. Even English varieties differ so much that they have been given different names, such as greyhound mountain fox, bush fox or cur fox. The differences lie in the colour, absolute size, and relative proportions of various parts of the body. The total length of the head and body of English foxes may differ to a very large extent, though the length of tail and ears is much less variable. There are thirteen recognised species of foxes, distributed widely over the world, and occupying a great variety of habitats. The foxes have the most extensive range of any Canidae. Unlike the wolves, they are found in Africa north of the Sahara as well as in central and southern Africa. They range all over Europe and Asia to some distance south of the Himalayas and as far east as Japan. In America, they are distributed from the far north, on the shores of Hudson Bay in Labrador, southwards to the latitude of North Mexico. The best known of the foxes is the common red fox.

With the foxes we should also mention the colishé, grey fox or Virginian fox, which is found in North America from Virginia to Texas, though it also occurs in Pennsylvania, Guatemala, Honduras, Costa Rica, and Yucatan. It is much less sagacious than the common fox, and also less destructive to the farmer. It feeds on birds and eggs, and will also catch small animals such as rabbits, cotton-rats, Florida rats and voles. It also eats insects and vegetable foods, especially ears of maize. Sometimes the colishé will climb trees to

The mountain fox, a variety of red fox. Foxes are the most widely distributed of all Canidae.

The fennec foxes' large ears, fairy-like faces, sandy colour and large, nocturnal eyes, give them great elegance and beauty. They can be seen in the nocturnal houses at many zoos.

avoid danger, especially when it is being hunted with hounds. Its odour is less penetrating than that of the European fox, but it gives good sport to huntsmen.

The Arctic foxes are definitely a distinct species on account of their external form, colouration, and change of hue, peculiarities of cranial form, of conformation, lack of odour and habits. These foxes range all through the Arctic regions. In summer the colour is a bluish or brownish grey but in winter some individuals, but only some, become entirely white. They are the only Canidae which change colour in the same way as the ermine and variable hare. Sometimes both white and grey cubs are found in the same litter. At the other extreme the fennec foxes are entirely desert-living, inhabiting North Africa from Nubia to Algiers and found throughout the Sahara. These little animals are very beautiful and recognisable by their very long ears. In captivity they are very tame and gentle. They are fond of dates and any sweet fruit, and eat eggs.

Another remarkable canid is the raccoon-like dog. These strange animals are sometimes classed with the foxes and live in Japan and parts of China. They inhabit woods on mountain slopes and are said to climb trees to get at the fruit. They rest in hollow tree-trunks and burrows and are of interest because, unlike other Canidae, under certain conditions they go into a form of hibernation like badgers. They only do this if they are fat and in very good condition, going to sleep during the winter in a deep burrow. If not hibernating in winter, they frequent running streams to feed on fish. They are omnivorous, feeding habitually on vegetable substances, largely acorns. They are also fond of fish and if given the choice of fish or meat will always eat the fish first. They are very timid and not at all savage, becoming used to human masters. They are also very clean. Their movements are somewhat civet-like and they sleep in a peculiar manner rolled up in a ball. Unlike in other dogs, the upper surface of the skull is strongly concave and the muzzle very pointed.

The dholes

Dholes of the genus *Cuon* are of two species, southern dholes and northern dholes. They are found from Siberia to Java. The dholes are larger than jackals but vary in size as well as colour. They have moderately long tails which may or may not be bushy. They normally live in forests, and are diurnal and gregarious, hunting in packs of six to twenty. They live largely on wild pigs and various kinds of deer such as sambur, spotted deer, antelope and even nilgai. They are savage and very brave and have even been known to kill a tiger. These so-called dogs are practically untameable and have a rank, disagreeable odour.

The bush dog

The bush dog is a very curious canid. It is believed to be of considerable antiquity and remains have been found in caverns with Pleistocene deposits in Brazil. These animals are remarkable for the shortness of their limbs and ears and for their very short tail and muzzle. The body is relatively long and so is the neck. They are omnivorous, but prefer meat to vegetable food. They are very bold and determined and dislike confinement. It is believed that they hunt in packs by scent and they can be very savage; however, they are rarely seen and take readily to water, though they never frequent the lowlands by the coast. The skull is notable for the shortness of the muzzle which has a swollen appearance between the forward margins of the orbits, or eye-sockets. The teeth are remarkable for the absence or minute size of the second upper molar in both jaws.

The Cape hunting or hyaena dog

The hyaena dogs, an African species, are so-called because of their markings, which somewhat resemble those of hyaenas. Like the true wolves they are plains hunting creatures which combine in packs to

Little is known of the life
and habits of the bush dogs,
found in the tropical forests
of Brazil and Guiana in
South America.

The bat-eared foxes are
found only in east and
central Africa.

pull down large game such as zebras; this they can only do because of their skill in social hunting tactics. These dogs reach the size of a tall greyhound, though their limbs are rather longer than most other Canidae and they are more thickset than greyhounds. Whatever their affinities, their hunting habits are very similar to those of true wolves, but they do not make burrows.

The bat-eared fox

The bat-eared foxes, also known as large-eared Cape dogs, are found only in eastern and southern Africa. They are one of the oddest of all Canidae, both on account of the number of teeth and as regards their general proportions. They are the size of a large fox and stand higher on the legs and have shorter, though equally bushy tails. The ears are very large as in the fennec foxes, but relatively broader.

Such then are the wolves' relations. The segregation of the Canidae into so many diverse forms which are still so closely related by all anatomical criteria is a remarkable story in evolutionary history. That such diversification could have occurred in so short a time, in evolutionary terms, indicates the genetic adaptability of this group of animals, possibly greater than any other. It is possibly their ability to diversify that has enabled man to breed so many dissimilar creatures as domestic dogs, perhaps derived from only some four closely related sub-species of the same foundation stock. Plainly, the canid family carries a great diversity of genes which can readily segregate and recombine to give different properties in the progeny. It may be of interest in this respect that wolves and dogs possess a greater number of chromosomes than any other known mammal, which may contribute to their great diversity. We shall see in a later chapter how all the cubs in a wolf litter have both morphological and temperamental differences which help them perform different tasks in their social organisation and pack hunting. Meanwhile, in the next chapter we shall see how wolves have adapted, anatomically and physiologically, to their place in the ecological scene.

Maned wolves, relaxed but alert. Note the slender features and the large ears.

Physical characteristics

Wolves and their close relatives have quickly spread over the face of the earth, have become adapted in different species and sub-species to a wide variety of situations and, man apart, have been one of the most successful groups of animals that nature has produced. It is really this success that has brought the clash with man, with whom wolves can certainly not compete. Clues to this success are given by the anatomy of wolves, by which we mean the northern grey wolves (the type species)—an anatomy which is shared by their descendants our domestic dogs; although of course domestic dogs show differences which have arisen as a result of domestication and specialised breeding.

In the Ice Age habitat, to which wolves were adapted, the herbivores on which they preyed were of three main types. Some were large and lumbering, like bison, but defended themselves by means of their horns and a defensive herd organisation; others were small and swift-moving, like deer; others were relatively large and swift, but without weapons of defence, like horses. To hunt such animals, a predator must possess speed and stamina. He must be equipped with powerful teeth and jaws, both for seizing the prey and for tearing and consuming the flesh. He must possess adequate sense organs, by which the prey can be located and followed. Furthermore, since many of the animals hunted are too large to be tackled by a lone wolf, the predators must be capable of organising themselves into packs and combining in the hunt. So there is a need for social organisation, intelligence, means of communication, and a hierarchy system with leaders and led.

The northern wolves vary quite considerably in size, according to the areas in which they live. The timber wolves of North America are somewhat larger than the grey wolves of northern Europe, in this respect resembling those from eastern Siberia. Even amongst the timber wolves, the size is variable, those from the more northerly

The head of *Canis lupus*.

87

Weights of some wolf specimens, according to published observations, given in pounds; based on a table in *The Wolf*, by L. David Mech.

regions being larger than those from the more southerly. Of all the wolves, the northern grey wolves are by far the largest, and their size is related to the larger prey which they attack in more northerly regions. Although much smaller than most of the prey animals which they take, they are big, powerful animals all the same, as is shown by the measurements below of wolf specimens, all taken from published observations. The weights are given in pounds.

The main features of the skeleton are illustrated on page 89. The limbs are long with strong slender bones, and as with all fast moving animals as we have already seen the gait is digitigrade—that is the

ADULTS ONLY (AT LEAST 1 YEAR OLD)

Location	Number	Sex	Average	Minimum	Maximum
Northwest Territories	18	M	98	90	116
Northwest Territories	21	F	85	70	110
Northwest Territories	80	M	97[2]	63[2]	133[2]
Northwest Territories	66	F	83[2]	50[2]	119[2]
Soviet Union	6	M	97	84	100
Soviet Union	6	F	75	–	96
Alaska	60	M	85[1]	60[1]	112[1]
Alaska	50	F	71[1]	54[1]	82[1]
Ontario	40	M	61	43	81
Ontario	33	F	54	39	70

[1] Skinned weights of animals over 1 year old. These are 10 to 15 pounds low, depending on size of animal.
[2] Primarily animals over 1 year old, but includes about 10 per cent pups.

ADULTS AND PARTLY GROWN PUPS

Location	Number	Sex	Average	Minimum	Maximum
Alaska	6	M	90	64	112
Alaska	9	F	67	50	80
Alaska	24	M	90	72	114
Alaska	20	F	72	55	93
Minnesota	84	M	78	50	114
Minnesota	60	F	61	45	84
Yugoslavia	?	?	73	–	139
Soviet Union	23	M	88	–	108
Soviet Union	23	F	74	–	90
Finland	52	M	89	57	121
Finland	33	F	70	53	99

wolves walk on the digits and not on the soles of the feet. There are four toes on each foot protected by soft, resilient pads. The fifth digit is retained as a dew claw, which enables the animal to dig in on the true foot and slow its progress on slippery surfaces such as mud or snow. As with other fast-moving animals, the clavicle or collarbone has been lost, so that the front of the body is supported on a sling formed by the two scapulae (shoulder blades) and their associated muscles, a shock absorber to give resilience during fast motion or when jumping. The non-retractile claws enable the animal to scramble up steep loose surfaces, and also to dig or enlarge burrows to form their dens. In the hind limb, the fibula is reduced in size so that the tibia provides rigidity, without power of rotation. This arrangement allows the powerful muscles of motion over the hindquarters and in the rear limb to provide a strong and quickly mobilised force for forward movement. In the forelimb, on the other hand, both radius and ulna are strong powerful bones, which permit some rotation of the limbs, useful in digging, tearing of flesh, and play. In the vertebral column, the spines of the vertebrae slope backwards to the last thoracic, after which they slope forwards. This

This typical canid skeleton has to be that of a fast-moving predator. Note the fine structure of the bones, particularly the limbs and ribs; the shape of the vertebral crests, backwards in front and forwards behind to a pivoted point; the single bones of the rear limbs, giving rigidity, while the double bones of the forelimbs permit rotation; the elongated muzzle, accommodating a powerful tooth mechanism.

indicates the pivotal point where the trunk bends when the animal is at full gallop. The ribs are finely constructed, but deep to accommodate a large heart and lungs, essential to so swift-moving a creature. The tail is long and powerful to act as a balancing organ during swift movement, and to be raised or depressed during various phases of social interplay. The bones of the vertebral column are cervical 7, thoracic 13, lumbar 7, sacral 3, coccygeal 20-23. This formula is fairly standard for most mammalian species.

Laymen often wonder how palaeontologists can construct a probable likeness of an entire animal from a few fragments of bone recovered from a fossil site. However, the shape and structure of wolf bones, even if only small fragments were available, would clearly show that this animal was a fast-moving and powerful predator. So beautifully is the architecture of the skeleton adapted to its purpose and the animal's way of life that this conclusion would be inevitable. The skull too is marvellously adapted for its purposes. The face and muzzle are long; the lips and cheeks fleshy and mobile, permitting a wide variety of facial expression essential in the wolf's social interactions. The upper and lower jaws are very powerful, providing ample space for the formidable tooth mechanisms used in seizing prey, tearing flesh, and crushing bones. There are sensitive tactile whiskers on the muzzle; the tongue is long and very mobile, so that flesh can be licked and water lapped. The long nasal passages provide the location for the organs of smell, so essential to an animal which uses its senses so extensively in tracking prey. A long muzzle is essential for this purpose, since no animals with short nasal passages (such as man and other primates) is equipped with the extremely sensitive sense of smell possessed by animals such as wolves. The eyes are large and set towards the side of the head in orbits which are not fully closed, as in man, by a bony ring. They provide keen sight, but vision is not fully binocular as in man. The long muzzle has another important part to play in the physiology of an Arctic-living animal. The nasal passages are provided with a rich blood supply, which ensures that air passing over them to the lungs is warmed before entering the respiratory passages. This effect is enhanced by the presence of large frontal sinuses which are filled with warmed air. These are situated in the so-called 'stop' which is a feature of the northern wolves, as opposed to the more southerly species, and which is so prominent in some breeds of our domestic dogs.

A wolf's muzzle and the orbits comprise nearly one-half of the length of the whole skull. Behind the muzzle is the cranium, constructed of a number of bones fused together to form the brain case. The bony structure is very strong and is covered by the powerful muscles of mastication. This serves two purposes. The head is well protected from injury, which could easily arise from the thrashing limbs of an animal that was being attacked. Secondly, the powerful jaw mechanisms require muscles of great strength, for their proper function. These muscles are accommodated also within three bony crests, which add further strength and rigidity and add further to the muscle-leverage. The paired frontal crests separate the muzzle from the cranium and the parietal crest divides the external surface of the cranium into two separate areas. The ears are set sideways and can be rotated, giving a good sense of hearing and of sound location.

The wolf's tooth mechanisms are unique in nature, being adapted to its methods of attack on prey animals. When members of the cat family attack their prey, this is done by a sudden spring, the claws—sharp, curved, retractile, and extremely dangerous—being used to obtain a purchase on the animal and to claw it to the ground. The wolf's claws, as we have seen, though useful for many purposes, are not designed as weapons of offence. In the cat family, the canine teeth are large and re-curved, and are used for locking on the neck

The head of a timber wolf howling.

91

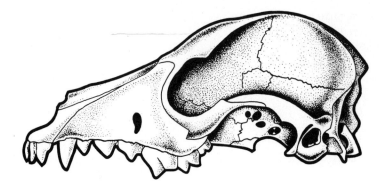

This canid skull shows well the features described in the text. Note the comparative lengths of muzzle and brain case; the arrangement of the teeth; the ridges and crests, to which the powerful muscles of mastication are attached, and which protect the brain case from injury.

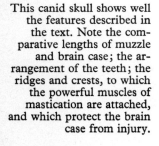

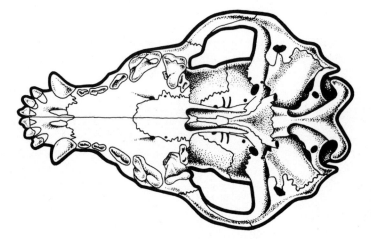

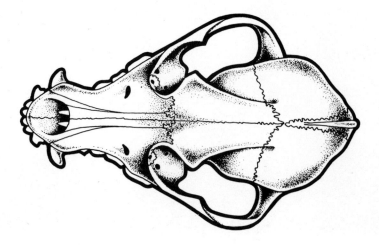

of the prey and pulling it over. The cats, however, are mostly much bigger in relation to their prey weight than are the wolves; for example, once a lion has sprung onto the back of a zebra and locked its fangs and claws on its flanks and neck, the zebra will fall and the prey is secured. Wolves, being much lighter in proportion to the prey weight, must lock their teeth onto whatever part of the body is attacked and must cling there while another wolf or wolves obtain a purchase on a different part of the body. In spite of all efforts of the prey animal to dislodge him, the wolf must retain his grip. This purpose is achieved by the extraordinary development of a trap-like structure comprising a combination of the incisor and canine teeth.

The incisors are all unusually large for a predatory animal and sub-divided into three parts, a central part and two lateral parts, by notches; a central part of the incisor is longer than the lateral parts and a row of incisor teeth is thus serrated. The upper corner incisors are elongated like the canines, with which they interlock, the whole mechanism resembling the teeth of a gin trap. Once locked on the prey these front teeth are never released, whatever efforts are made by the victim to dislodge the wolf. Locked, say, on to the snout of a bison, a victim will toss its head throwing the wolf clear off the ground, shaking it, and propelling it downwards again. Just as a bulldog will hold on to the snout of the bull it is baiting until maybe it is killed, so the wolf hangs on to its prey. This is made possible only by the beautifully designed mechanisms of the front teeth apparatus, unique in nature. The effect is enhanced by the gap between the canines and the pre-molars, known as the diastema; the first premolars are reduced in size adding further to the effect.

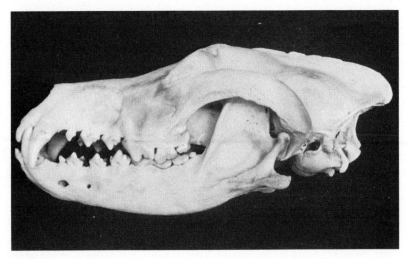

The deadly tooth apparatus.

Further back are the teeth used for crushing and tearing. In the upper jaw the fourth premolar, and in the lower the first molar, are fused with the succeeding molar to form the carnassial teeth, which are so powerful that not only can flesh be rent but bones crushed. Here again we find a contrast with the feline predators, since although they too have carnassial teeth, animals such as lions can only crush small bones such as vertebrae and ribs; they cannot crush the long limb bones which wolves readily tackle. Wolves' teeth are subject to much wear throughout their lives, and in old age they have difficulty in pulling down and consuming their prey. This may well be one reason why wolves sometimes turn to capturing and eating small domestic animals such as sheep and goats.

The skin of the wolf also is adapted to the cold climatic regions they inhabit. It is very loose over the back of the trunk and the neck, and the coat is very thick and deeply furred. The coat is shed in the autumn and replaced by very thick fur to withstand winter conditions, a lighter coat being developed again in the spring. The cubs shed their puppy fur at six months old and develop adult winter pelage. Sebaceous glands are present, but are not numerous except at the lips, anus, back surface of the trunk, and over the sternum. Sweat glands only occur in the digital pads. Body cooling is effected, as in dogs, by panting, that is by drawing air over the large and flexible tongue. There are two scent glands on each side of the anus, which are important to wolves in identifying one another and in territorial marking. The brain of the wolf is small by human standards, but nevertheless, if it is compared to the brains of herbivorous animals, it will be seen that the cerebral hemispheres are prolonged at the back so as to cover most of the cerebellum. Wolves are undoubtedly extremely intelligent and this is probably correlated with the large cerebrum. The olfactory lobes are well developed, a correlation with the keen sense of smell.

Wolves have large and distensible stomachs which are somewhat pear-shaped; this adaptation is necessary to their habits of gorging and of using the stomach for conveying meat to the cubs.

In general terms, the wolf's anatomy is rather unspecialised in the sense that it conforms closely to the ancestral mammalian pattern. However it is specialised in certain ways, and adapted to the way of life for which the wolf was evolved, namely that of a plains predator living in a cold climate.

The various sub-species of wolves, coyotes, jackals, and the more primitive breeds of domestic dog cannot be readily differentiated by means of skeletal features. Their differentiation depends on size, colour, the nature of the coat, and features concerned with the tail. The northern grey wolf, which we have been studying, is the largest

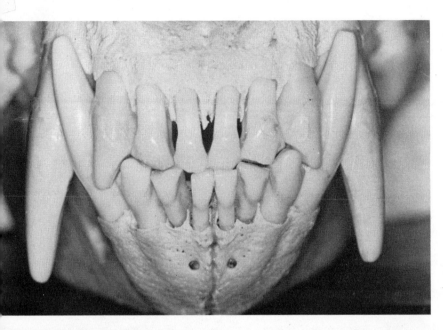

Note how the large canines together with the incisors constitute a trap-like mechanism which, once closed, prevents escape even by the strongest animals.

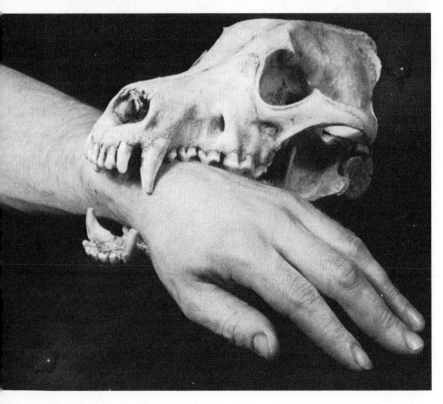

The extent of a wolf's grasp with its jaws. Note how worn teeth can become—old wolves have great difficulty in securing prey, and it is often they who take to feeding on small domestic stock.

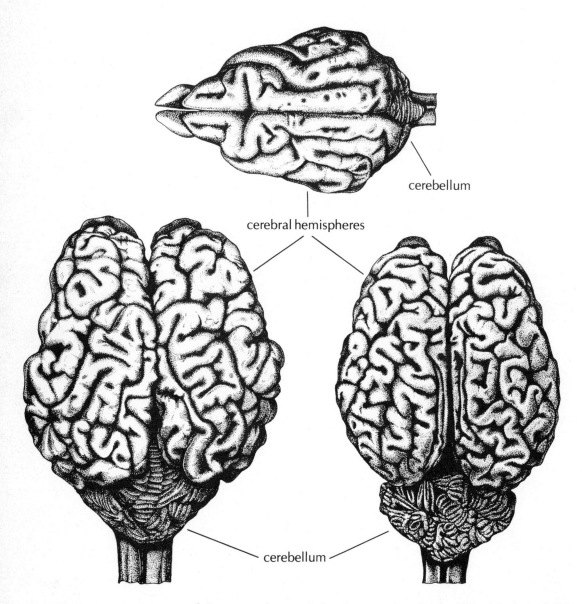

cerebellum

cerebral hemispheres

cerebellum

Brains of wolf (top), ox (left) and horse (right). Note the prolongation backwards of the wolf's cerebral hemispheres, compared with the herbivores. The cerebrum is the seat of intelligence (not to scale).

of the true wolves and also the most heavily furred, with the possible exception of the Tibetan wolf, *Canus lupus chanco*, which has the alternative name of *Canus lupus laniger*, meaning woolly coated. The Tibetan wolves, which live in the high and bitterly cold mountainous areas of Tibet and the Himalayas, stretching into northern Kashmir, have to cope with even harsher conditions than the grey wolves living in the Arctic Circle. The pale-footed Asian wolves and the Arab desert wolves are smaller, slighter, thinner-coated with short hairs, and more slenderly built. There are also temperamental differences, particularly between wolves and jackals which are far less aggressive and are more given to a life of scavenging. The differentiation of skeletal remains is of special importance to students who wish to determine whether bones found in early human settlements are those of wolves or of domesticated dogs. There has been, and there still is, controversy over canid remains from early Neolithic settlements of the Near East, such as Jericho.

Much has been made of a claim originally advanced as long ago as 1892 by the biologists Goudry and Boule, who stated that in wolves the length of the upper carnassial teeth is greater than that of the two molars, measured together, whereas in the dog and jackal the length of the carnassial is less than, or at the most equal to, the length of the two molars. However, the pale-footed Asian wolves were advanced as an exception to this rule, so that it plainly would not apply in Near Eastern situations where these were the only wolves found. In order to resolve the problem, Juliet Clutton-Brock produced a graph, shown on page 98, which gave measurements of a limited number of skulls showing the relationships between the carnassials and the molars. Those of the skulls which showed the greater size of the carnassial over the two molars are to the left of the axis line, and those in which the two molars are of greater size than the carnassials are to the right. This certainly shows that most grey wolves from the north had the carnassials larger than the molars, the pale-footed Asian wolves and Arabian wolves are rather variable, whereas domestic dogs and jackals have the molars larger than the carnassials.

The controversy appears to this author at any rate to be somewhat academic. Dogs were domesticated from wolves in northern countries long before they appeared in domestication in the Near East. Indeed, by that time diminutive breeds of domestic dogs had already been developed in the so-called turbary dogs of the Swiss lake settlements. Furthermore, dingo stock had been introduced to Australia by at least 18,000 B.C. In any case, it is relevant to ask, what is meant by domestication? The dingos provide a case in point. Except that they are perhaps lighter and slightly shorter-legged than the pale-footed Asian wolves they are otherwise identical with them. In Australia, until rendered nearly extinct because of their raids on sheep stations, they lived a completely wild life behaving and preying on the fauna as do the Asian wolves. The Aborigines stole their cubs and brought them up as hunting and guard dogs. Can this be regarded as domestication? Can these animals, which are given a specific name of *Canis familiaris dingo*, be really regarded as domestic dogs or are they in fact wolves, and should they be classified as *Canis lupus dingo*?

Assuredly, they are descended from wolf cubs brought to Australia by the Aborigines in their migrations, which subsequently escaped and returned to a wild existence. In this respect, they are surely wolves which were for a time in captivity, and the relationship between carnassial and molar sizes as given in Clutton-Brock's table shows a similar ratio to that of the pale-footed Asian wolves.

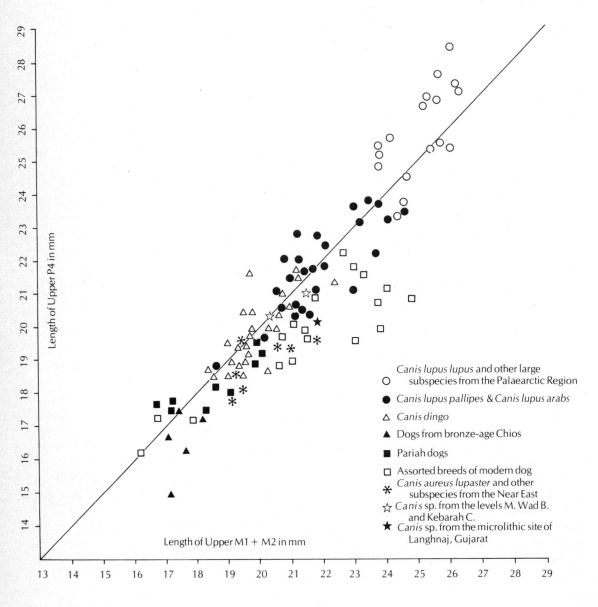

Domesticated or not ? The dingo of Australia.

At the other end of the scale, husky dogs of Greenland and Alaska are plainly very close to wolves, and indeed the natives every few generations release a husky bitch when on heat so that it can be covered by wild-living wolves and thus breed back to their original stock. Although they are raised in captivity, no attempt is made to improve the breed, but rather to retain the features of the wild forebears by back-breeding. Nevertheless, the huskies show some features characteristic of domesticated dogs. For example, they come in season at irregular intervals, according to some authors twice a year as in domestic dogs. (One should note perhaps that owners of huskies in the United Kingdom state that their bitches, though irregular, come on heat once a year only.)

Evidently, there are degrees of domestication between the wild animal that is caught and used and animals which are selectively bred for some particular feature or quality. There may be a third distinction, that of the feral dogs, that is to say breeds which have been domesticated and which have gone secondarily wild, such as the pariah dogs, which scavenge the cities of the Near to Far East. Such dogs show evidence of former domestication, in that they come

The graph, opposite, shows the relationship of the length of the upper carnassial tooth to the combined lengths of the upper first and second molars in dogs, wolves and jackals, and in canid specimens from Natufian levels in Palestine. The larger carnassials are to the left of the line.

on heat twice a year, they have sloppy ears and some have small curly tails unlike those of wolves. In wolves, the tail is always straight, well furred, and hangs down when at rest to cover the anus. Even to this day, many of the less specialised breeds of domestic dogs readily revert to the wild, form themselves into packs, and hunt suitable game. For example, packs of the native yellow dogs, allied to basenjis, run wild in the Athi Plains Game Reserve near Nairobi in Kenya, and are a nuisance because they kill the young of Thompson's gazelles and other wild species which are preserved there. This kind of situation is not peculiar to dogs. For example, in Britain the pony stocks run wild in forested areas and are rounded up annually for branding and for selection of those required to be broken and used as domestic animals. In America, imported domestic horses escaped, ran wild, and quickly re-populated the former plains habitats of wild horses, as mustangs.

In the more advanced and specialised breeds of domestic dogs, there is obviously no difficulty in separating them by anatomical features from the parent wolves. In some, such as pekingese, the numbers of teeth have become reduced, and the dental formula is such that they could not strictly be included in the genus *Canis*. Such animals, should they escape and decide to go feral, could obviously not combine in packs to prey on wild animals. They are, therefore, sports or anomalies produced by deliberate selection of attributes that make them unfit for existence, except when dependent on man. They are recognisably *Canis*, but are outside the natural scheme of evolution and the normal rules of taxonomy cannot be applied to them.

Such freaks apart, all wolves (including coyotes), jackals, and domestic dogs share an anatomy that is so similar as to render it difficult or impossible to differentiate them from their skeletons alone. Domestication of itself, without selective breeding, may create certain differences, such as the reduction in the size of the carnassial teeth, and it is said that when wolves are bred in captivity changes are observable even in the second to third generation in some shortening of the muzzle and a reduction in the length of leg. Changes in the regularity of the heat periods, as with the huskies, also possibly arise in the first place because of a changed way of life. One must further recall that all cubs in a single wolf litter differ considerably from each other in size, coat colour, and temperament. Only those cubs which take readily to life in captivity and contact with man will be reared, and this from the start introduces an element of selection for docility, perhaps for imbecility. Some attributes which are common in domestic dogs can be attributed to neoteny, that is the retention into adult life of traits which are present in wolf cubs but not in adult wolves. Such features are the floppy ears of dogs such as spaniels, the tendency of the tails to curl, and the habit of domestic dogs of barking. Wolf cubs frequently bark, but adult wolves rarely do so, although a statement often made that they never bark is untrue.

This being the case, it can be seen that in domesticating dogs man has not introduced anything which was not present in the parent stock, except in so far as he has perpetuated some pathological

The coyotes of North America—in reality small wolves living in the same areas as wolves. However, their feeding habits are different, so that wolves and coyotes do not normally compete.

deformities, such as the shortened skulls of pekingese and boxers, which would be lethal in a wild animal. Differences of coat colour and hair character are all represented in the ancestral genes and it was only necessary for man to breed from those animals possessed of certain tendencies to establish them as a breed feature. The same can be said of the abilities of dogs for sight- or scent-hunting, for herding, for ferocity or docility and so on.

The anatomy of the wolf, then, is the result of natural selection in producing an intelligent, social, animal equipped to combine in packs for hunting of large animals, of much greater size than the wolf itself, and to withstand the rigours of the various habitats in which they are found. There is much variability within a single family, let alone between breeds, and it is this which man has been able to exploit to produce the multifarious breeds of domestic dog. It is perhaps worth noting that a variability such as this which man also reveals is only possible within a monogamous system of mating. In animals such as horses, a single male will acquire anything from twenty to fifty mares, and thus imprint his own stamp on the progeny, which therefore show great uniformity. Greater variability, essential to wolves in their methods of hunting and acquiring food, is only possible when many sires produce the younger generations.

The red wolf of North America.

Food and hunting methods

The grey wolf and its close kinsman the timber wolf, which appeared only recently in evolutionary terms at the beginning of the Pleistocene, were clearly adapted originally to life in the great wastes of the tundra. The vast extent of the tundra at that time supported a characteristic fauna of large herbivorous animals, many of which— such as the mammoth and woolly rhinoceros—are now extinct. Others, such as reindeer, caribou, musk ox and elk, survive but their range is restricted to the far north where tundra conditions persist. These were large animals, well able to escape from predators or to defend themselves. Furthermore, the open nature of the terrain made it impossible to capture prey by concealment and stealth, and neither of the two main tundra predators, wolf and man, developed sufficient fleetness of foot to run down the prey; they were also much smaller than most of the prey they captured. It followed that a predator, to be successful, must be endowed with rather special qualities. The point has already been made, but deserves re-emphasis.

An essential feature of tundra life was the necessity for seasonal migration. During the Arctic winter, blizzards rendered life impossible except for small rodents which could live under the snow on deep frozen vegetable material. At this time the great herds moved south and their predators went with them, returning when the warmth of spring laid bare the rich, well-watered vegetation, on which they subsisted. During the summer, food sources were plentiful because, in addition to the large game animals, there were abundant small rodents, hares, wildfowl and fish. To the wolves, these additional resources were essential to life—they were unable to follow the large prey to the limits of their northward migrations because of the necessity to raise a family once a year. For half the year, the wolf must have a stable home range of sufficient size to provide the needs of the family.

Another view of a red wolf, giving voice in the manner characteristic of all true wolves.

Both wolf and man became adapted in different ways to meet these *They* challenges. In one way, their development was similar. Both developed a highly organised social system, advanced intelligence, powers to communicate with their mates and to combine in hunting. Man, originally mostly vegetarian from sub-tropical and tropical regions, faced the greater challenge, and he developed greater intelligence and greater sophistication in his hunting methods. He learned to trap and corral his prey and could select from the herds those animals he fancied most, usually those in prime condition; he could, and did, at times indulge in mass slaughter. Above all, man learned to make and use offensive weapons by which he could kill his prey from afar. The wolves inevitably took the weak, the maimed and sick; in this way they developed a more rational and advantageous relationship with the prey species. Indeed, it is today generally conceded that the depredations of the wolves are beneficial in preserving the vigour of the species on which they prey. —

At the end of the Pleistocene and the beginning of the Holocene, the extent of the tundra became much restricted as the ice fringes receded. This forced both wolf and man to find ways of living in habitats to which they were not accustomed and were less well adapted. Only in the far north do wolves, and man in the shape of Eskimos, still live in Ice Age conditions. Thus we find wolves widespread in a narrow circle around the Arctic from western Europe, through Siberia to Alaska and northern Canada. This is still a very large area. Their habits have been studied in these areas by Canadian, American, and Russian observers, and we find a remarkable degree of uniformity in the accounts from different countries.

South of the tundra, two main habitats were occupied by the wolf populations. The first was the great belt of grassland, prairie, and steppe, which was developed on the black chernozem soils stretching right across North America, through eastern Asia and Europe to the Black Sea region. This was still open country suited to the hunting methods of wolf and man. Man remained nomadic, and the wolf suffered little change in his way of life. Grazing animals remained prolific, in the shape of horses, buffalo, deer and antelope. The second new habitat consisted of mountain and forest, and this proved far less congenial to either predator. Man forsook his nomadic habits and lived in permanent settlements. He learned to clear the forests and developed agriculture and stock husbandry. The wolves lived in the forests and caught there as much prey as they could. However, the food resources were inadequate for their voracious appetites, and had to be supplemented by raiding outside the forest limits. Inevitably, this meant making attacks on man's newly acquired domestic animals.

All the evidence goes to show that in the tundra man and wolf lived in amicable relations, but with the change of the habitat the wolf threatened man's new way of life and great efforts were made to exterminate him. In order to understand the wolf problem, therefore, it is necessary to study his ways in the three different habitats in which he now exists, namely, the tundra, steppes and prairies, and woodland and mountain. In doing so we are still considering the northern grey and timber wolves, remembering that long ago sub-species of wolves were developed, adapted to other habitats than tundra. Such are the red wolves of Texas, the mountain wolves of Tibet, the Asian savannah wolves, the desert wolf of Arabia and others. Man's main conflict has been with the grey wolves outside their natural area.

Wolves of the tundra

The year of the wolf is divided into two sharply demarcated periods. From the early spring until the autumn, wolves live a settled existence in a tundra territory and raise their young. From the autumn and through the winter, they are nomadic and follow the large prey herds. Unlike the domestic dog, wolves come in season once a year only and the cubs are ready to join the seasonal migration when they are six months old. The male wolves mate at the age of three, the females when two. This ensures that the females are mated to older and stronger males. However, no wolf mates, male or female, until a territory is acquired, and wolves without a territory remain celibate. Even so, celibate wolves remain members of the family circle, and perform useful tasks, as helping to hunt, rear and teach the cubs, and 'baby-sit'. Some wolves, it is said, seem to prefer 'uncle' or 'aunt' status. Once mated, wolves, as we have already seen, are monogamous and stay with one partner for life, although as with man it is said that aberrations of fidelity do sometimes occur. If one member of a pair dies or is killed, the other partner usually joins the celibates. The wolf family consists of an adult female, an adult male, the cubs or sub-adults—rarely more than five, one to three yearlings, and the uncles and aunts with no territory. These combine to form the pack.

During the spring and summer, the wolf family lives within its territory, an area in tundra conditions of at least one hundred square miles. The boundaries are scent-marked at marking posts with urine or faeces, refreshed every week or so. Territories are respected by other wolves, though occasionally a wolf from a neighbouring territory places a marker on his neighbour's land, seemingly just for the fun of it! The territories are transected by wolf trails, these being the routes which the wolves habitually follow when they go out on their hunting forays. Along these trails there may be caches of meat. The family must find its subsistence during the summer months entirely from this territory. Between March and June, the caribou or reindeer are passing over the territory and form the wolves' main source of food. At this time, the female is entirely occupied with whelping, suckling and tending the cubs, and takes no part in the hunting. The male members of the pack, which may be two or more, set up a howling session some time between 4.00 and 7.00 in the evening and depart for the nightly hunt. They return next morning, or, if the hunting is poor, not till the afternoon of the following day. During the night's hunting they cover forty miles or more.

When the caribou or reindeer are located, the wolves make no effort at concealment, but mingle openly with the herds. The caribou stolidly ignore them, for they know—and so do the wolves—that they can easily outrun them and have nothing to fear; even a three-month-old caribou calf can easily get away from a wolf. The wolves will often

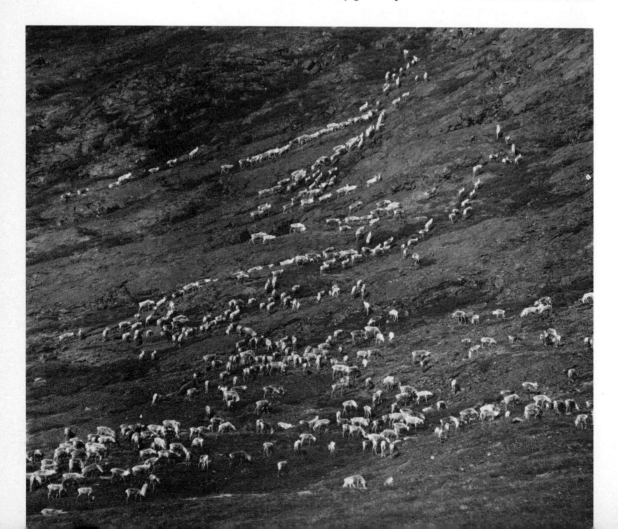

chase a caribou, but if unsuccessful in overtaking it rarely pursue for more than a few hundred yards, at the most a mile or so. It has been observed that wolves may make ten or twelve unsuccessful attacks before they succeed in bringing down an animal. Meanwhile the wolves patiently probe the herds seeking for an animal that is sick or maimed. They are very clever at locating such animals, but the caribou also tend to conceal them in the centre of their herds. It usually takes the wolves upwards of four hours to locate an animal suitable for attack.

The wolves move at an easy lope of five or six miles per hour, conserving their strength. Once the prey is located, the wolves use their herding instinct—bred into our sheepdogs—to manoeurve the herd, gradually isolating the victim. Once the victim is isolated, the attack begins. One wolf makes a decoy attack from the front, attempting to seize the nose. When this is successful, the second wolf attacks from the rear—the serious attack meant to bring down the animal. In the case of caribou, this usually takes the form of a violent charge

Caribou, opposite, are probably the most important prey animals of North American wolves. They are very fleet—it is mostly the very young, elderly or sick which are caught.

Wolves also eat small rodents such as the ground squirrel, especially in summer when the need to raise a family prevents them from following the grazing herds.

at the shoulder, which knocks the caribou to the ground; the throat is then seized and the jugular vein is quickly opened. With caribou, the kill is quick and clean, though the wolf must avoid the thrashing hooves which are dangerous. With bigger and more dangerous game, the tail may be seized and twisted to bring the animal to the ground or an attempt may be made to sever an achilles tendon. Once killed, the carcass is dismembered. Some of the meat may be concealed in a cache somewhere close along the wolf trail. As much as can be consumed, in the case of a large wolf as much as thirty pounds, is swallowed and disgorged at a cache near the den where the female and her cubs are waiting. The female collects her rations from the cache, taking into the den only what she needs for immediate consumption.

After a time, when the cubs emerge from the den for play, the female becomes bored and indicates that she too wishes to join the hunting forays. One of the other males will then stay behind to watch the cubs, while she joins the nightly hunt. About June, the time will come when the caribou have passed through the territory and other sources of food must be utilised. At this time, the cubs are removed from the den to a rearing area. Since they are no longer suckling, they require water and this must be near by. At this time the wolves feed mostly on small rodents, such as mice and lemmings, and ground squirrels, which resemble the more southerly gophers. These small mammals become very abundant during the summer and the wolves especially relish the ground squirrel, which may weigh up to two pounds. They also lure wildfowl by various decoy antics, and they catch fish making their spawning runs up the rivers.

Their fishing techniques show the high intelligence of wolves. In some parts, they catch salmon by pawing them out of the water, as do bears also, when in shallow streams and exhausted at the end of their run. They also fish for jackfish or northern pike, which may weigh up to sixty pounds. At spawning time, these fish invade the intricate network of narrow channels in boggy marshes along the shores of the lakes. The wolves enter one of the larger channels and proceed upstream with a great deal of splashing. The fish are driven upstream into narrower and shallower channels; at last realising the danger, they make a dash for open water only to be snapped up by the wolves' jaws. They also catch 'suckers', but their technique is different. The suckers are sluggish and the wolves crouch on rocks where the stream is shallow and snatch them as they pass. The Arctic sculpin are also caught. These fish lurk under rocks in shallow water; the wolves wade into the water and overturn the rocks with paws or nose, catching the fish as they attempt to escape. The wolves will even take some shellfish from the streams.

When the caribou return in the autumn, intelligence appears to be relayed by lupine telegraph, so that the territory holders are aware of their approach before their actual arrival. The cubs have received their first instruction in hunting, toying at first with dead, then half-dead rodents. Now has come the time when they can go out with their parents to practise on the real thing. Their parents watch their first blundering attempts to catch an active healthy caribou, and gradually school them in the art of selecting the right animal, then isolating and attacking it in concert. At this time of the year, also, the wolves eat a certain amount of plant material, being very fond of some of the autumn berries.

From the autumn to the end of the winter, pack-hunting tends to replace the individual attack by a lone wolf or a pair of wolves. In this form of attack, several wolves acting in concert separate a small herd and drive it into an ambush, where other wolves are waiting. Alternatively, they will chase the caribou in relay, a fresh wolf lying in wait to take over the chase when the original pursuers get tired. In this form of hunting, more or less healthy animals will be taken, not only the sick and maimed; however, the herds selected are usually of mixed does and fawns, or of aged and sterile does. The prey may also be chased into places where they get wedged in rocks or fall over cliffs. They are also driven into water, but the wolf is no match for the caribou or deer in water; however, they intelligently anticipate where the animal will emerge, and other wolves are waiting for it at this point. Deer and caribou are especially vulnerable when on crusted ice overlying soft snow, since their feet sink in whereas the wolves' pads are more able to secure a grip.

In the more northerly areas, such as Alaska, there is a greater range of large prey animals, such as musk ox and moose. These animals are better able to defend themselves than are caribou, and even a pack of five or six wolves will hesitate to attack an adult moose since though they can probably overcome it a number of them will get injured. So long as the moose stands its ground, it is relatively safe; if however he turns and runs, the wolves will pursue and generally catch him. An injured wolf is usually killed by his mates and eaten; even if suffering from a minor wound, a wolf will avoid other wolves until it is healed. The methods by which wolves secure large and dangerous prey will be considered with the prairie habitat.

When the caribou move south, the wolf packs go with them and their territories are abandoned until the following season. Each family travels as a unit, though several family units may join together temporarily to form a band. Contact with the caribou is carefully maintained, though different bands, by some scent-marking arrangement, travel by different routes so as not to overlap. In northern

Canada and western Russia, bands rarely exceed five to ten individuals, though in Siberia up to a hundred may be seen together. The size of the band is probably related to the economics of the situation, since too big a band would not secure sufficient meat from a single victim to feed them all. The wolves now leave the tundra and enter the wooded taiga, where they continue to prey on the caribou but also feed on snowshoe hares, of which they are very fond.

In the taiga, the wolves come in contact with so-called civilised man. It is a time of danger, when they are away from their natural habitat. In the recent past, bounties were offered by the federal and state governments of 10-30 dollars for each wolf killed. Wolves were caught in traps and, although this is illegal, poisoned with strychnine baits. The fur-trappers who operate in the taiga are mortally and irrationally afraid of the wolves, and make exaggerated claims about the devastating numbers of caribou that they kill. The animals are also hunted by aeroplane. When located in open places such as a frozen lake, they are chased to exhaustion; the plane is then landed so that the 'sportsmen' may despatch the unfortunate wolves. The same technique is used also against the caribou, except that the caribou are mown down from the air by automatic weapons, and the wolves are blamed for the slaughter.

Wolf mortality at this time is high, affecting chiefly the younger wolves and those born in the previous spring. Many of the older wolves learn to avoid the traps and bait, showing great acumen. Owing to their high rate of reproduction, the wolf stocks can probably withstand these depredations, so long as they are left unmolested in

The musk ox survives only in Canada and Greenland, in the very far north, living on sparse vegetation in the inhospitable habitat shown here. At night they form a circle, with the cows and calves in the centre.

their permanent homes in the tundra, and so long as the caribou is not so depleted by man that there is not enough food for them. Here, too, they are threatened because man blames his own inroads on the caribou on the wolves.

Wolves of the steppes and prairies

When the ice receded at the end of the Ice Age, there were left to the south of the taiga the great areas of open plains and grasslands. These developed a characteristic fauna of large grazing animals, different from those which inhabit the tundra. In Europe there were wild horses, bison, saiga antelope, and many species of deer. In North America, there were bison (buffalo) and possibly, until the coming of man in the shape of Amerindians, horses also, white-tailed deer, and prong-horn antelope. This was open country, well-watered, and suited to wolves as predators of large animals in open country. In these areas, there was no need for wolves to indulge in their seasonal migrations, so that they lived and bred in the same area all the year round. In America, these wolves were known by the early buffalo hunters as buffalo wolves.

In the American prairies, the main prey animal was the buffalo, or bison as it is known in Europe. Wolves also preyed on the European bison, which like the American is also nearly extinct. The buffaloes are large and strong animals, which fight to the end. At night, they form a circle facing outwards, a palisade of horns facing the attacker; the young and the females and the weak are placed in

The moose, found only in North America, is a dangerous animal for wolves to attack. Even a pack of six wolves will leave a bull-moose, or a cow with calf, alone if it shows fight.

the centre. Domestic cattle in Africa adopt this same formation in places where there is danger of attack by hyaenas. During the day-time, when the buffalo are on the move, the wolves would lope along on the flanks of the herd seeking, as with the caribou, a weakened animal to attack.

The buffaloes are attacked by the wolves in relays. The primary attack is usually made by two wolves. One, often the female, makes the decoy attack from the front, attempting to seize the nose or lolling tongue. This is the same tactic as with the caribou, but the buffalo is a much stronger and more aggressive animal. He will throw his head in the air in an attempt to dislodge his attacker; but the wolf never releases his victim, even if thrown into the air; the trap-like teeth have locked and do not let go. The main attack by one or more wolves comes from the rear; an attempt is made to hamstring the animal, or to seize the tail. If the tail is seized, it is twisted to one side in an attempt to throw the animal to the ground; alternatively, as Russian observers have recorded, the animal is pulled backwards by the tail, which is suddenly released so that the animal pitches forward on to its nose. Sometimes the testes are seized and the animal may be emasculated; old hunters used to tell of ox buffalo in the herds, of large size and with woolly coats, which had been castrated by the

wolves. When attacked by more than two wolves the buffalo had little chance of escape, but evidently a number did escape, as is evidenced by the presence of these ox buffalo. Wolves were rarely able to make a clean kill of buffalo, as with caribou, and the unfortunate animal, fighting to the end, was virtually torn to pieces.

Attacks were also made on deer and antelope, which sometimes joined buffalo herds for protection. When attacking antelope, the wolves would often use guile. Antelope are full of curiosity and a wolf would hide itself, exposing some part of its body, perhaps the white underfur, so as to arouse this curiosity; when it came too close, the wolf would spring at it. All the resources of the wolf's armoury are used in hunting deer and antelope no less than caribou—teamwork, decoys, relays and ambushes. The prey are driven over cliffs or into rivers or lakes. The wolves also attempt to confuse them by howling in relays from different directions.

Once the 'buffalo wolves' preyed on enormous herds of bison, opposite, on the prairies of North America, large powerful beasts defeated only by a concerted attack by several wolves.

The European elk, smaller than the bull-moose, but very similar.

In Russia, deer and elk are also taken. They are driven until they collapse on the ice or are wedged among rocks. Animals are also easily captured when the earth is covered by deep snow with a crusty surface, since the hooves of deer and goats sink while the wolves with their broader paws and softer soles do not. Wolves also hunt hares, black grouse, geese and ducks. Other prey are bustards, corsac foxes, badgers, polecats, foxes and dogs. They will even eat amphibians and reptiles, berries and fruit. Russian observers, however, state that wolves will never attack large wild boars which roam alone, even in a pack. In the steppes, they also take a great deal of domestic stock from the nomadic peoples.

In steppe and prairie, therefore, although the habitat was altered with the recession of the ice, the wolves still found conditions which suited them. The early hunters between 1800 and 1850 in the United States did not attack the wolves which they did not fear, and the wolves were unafraid of them. Indeed, the sound of a gun would summon the wolves to share in the buffalo feast. They would stand at a respectful distance of fifty or sixty yards waiting for the flaying and butchering to be completed, and rush in to finish the remains when the hunters left. It is even recorded that, though shy by day, at night they would come into the purlieus of the camp and sit there, a dozen together, howling hideously for hours. To this day the wolves of Alaska sometimes indulge in this kind of behaviour. After the wolves began to be shot, they developed an uncanny instinct for keeping just out of rifle range. However, it was not the shooting which eliminated the wolves from the prairie habitat, but destruction of their main food source, the buffalo, a destruction in part deliberately undertaken to exterminate the other major predator of the buffalo, the Amerindian. In Russia, the steppes are largely peopled by nomads, so that interference with the wolves has been less destructive.

The forest of the taiga, home of the elk and other prey; nevertheless, in forest conditions wolves are often forced to make inroads on domestic stock for food. This is not their chosen habitat.

Wolves of the forests and mountains

So far as possible, wolves have avoided forests and the wooded taiga. In Russia, they penetrate the forest taiga massifs only along river valleys or in the wake of man through forest clearings. Where bears are numerous, wolves are scarce and vice versa, because they are opposites in selection of habitat. Wolves do not care for mountains, if plains habitats are available to them. Sometimes they frequent desert belts, but cling to river valleys, where the reeds provide them with refuge from which they emerge for long hunts.

Wolves are found at sea level along the Caspian and the Caucasian coast of the Black Sea. They are abundant too on the plateaux, attracted by small prey, such as the steppe marmots, ground squirrels

and picas. They frequent the sub-alpine belts of the Altai and Caucasus Mountains, and in the Tien Shan Mountains they are found at altitudes of 8,500 to 10,500 feet, from the conifer and birch belt to the upper juniper belt. In the Caucasus, the wolves are concentrated in mountainous forests, an unnatural habitat which gives rise to many problems. Their main food is said to be domestic cattle, wild boar and fish. There is also a Caucasian Game Reservation, throughout which wolves are uniformly distributed, though in the winter months they live mostly in broad-leaved forest, preying on the large population of boar, roe-deer, and deer. At other times, some 30 per cent are found in the alpine zone, 32 per cent in dark coniferous forest, and 38 per cent in broad-leaved forest. The loss of young boar, deer, roe-deer, chamois, and Caucasian buck has been estimated at 34 to 61 per cent in a five-month season, a heavy toll of the new generation of animals. Even so, the wolves also kill hundreds of domestic stock on the borders of the reservation, proving the point that a forest habitat cannot provide sufficient food for the support of these animals.

It has been ascertained from estimates made on fossil material in the Caucasus that since the recession of the ice the numbers of wolves first decreased in proportion to the decrease in wild ungulates; they again increased with the development of cattle breeding. However, the improvement of firearms and methods of capture, together with the breeding of large dogs for herd protection, seem again to have reduced the numbers.

Thus, in the Caucasus the wolves are confined to a forest habitat. Although they make heavy inroads on the young of forest animals, there is insufficient food for them, and they are forced to make raids from their forest shelter on domestic herds on the forest fringes. A similar situation formerly existed in Britain and Ireland, and certain other European countries. Before the 17th century, settlement of the land was largely in open low-lying country, and large areas of hills and woodlands remained undisturbed. It was in these areas that the wolves were confined; food was insufficient for them and they made depredations—and indeed serious inroads—on the herds of cattle and flocks of sheep. This was particularly serious in Scotland, where the people had little wealth other than their livestock. True mountain animals, such as wild sheep and goats, are far too agile for wolves, and are rarely caught unless injured. In spite of bounties, hunting and trapping, extinction of the wolves only came with destruction of their habitats.

Throughout the U.S.S.R. losses of stock and money from wolves are very great. They take camels, horses, cattle, sheep, and goats. They also attack and eat domestic dogs, which they steal from the villages. In America too trouble was experienced from so-called 'renegade' wolves. These were animals, old or maimed, with toes or feet missing as a result of escaping from a trap. They were solitary wolves which found a range and killed domestic stock as much for the sake of killing as for food. They were of great sagacity and, although ruthlessly hunted and destroyed when caught, appear to have been regarded with a certain degree of affection and admiration, and were even given pet names; their tracks could usually be identified by their deformities. They were uncanny in the way they avoided traps or poison, and seemed to know whether a man was armed or not. They made serious inroads on stock, mostly calves.

Unlike coyotes, wolves do not like putrid or dried animal remains. However, when pressed they will consume carrion. In addition, although they virtually never attack living human beings, they are not averse to exhuming and consuming human corpses. Such behaviour was formerly reported from Scotland, where the wolves may well have been hungry; it also occurred with well-fed wolves in North America. This is a very strange behavioural trait in an animal normally averse to carrion.

The skeleton of a Canadian elk or wapiti, virtually stripped by wolves. Nevertheless an optimistic coyote is happy to scavenge anything that is left. Coyotes themselves are too small to kill such prey.

Some interesting analyses of stomach contents from North American wolves show to what straits they are sometimes driven.

In 72 stomachs of red Texan wolves, 70 from Texas and 2 from Oklahoma, the chief food items were cotton-tail rabbits (*Sylvilagus*), domestic stock, rodents and carrion, in that order. The domestic stock included sheep, horses, cows, goats, calves and hogs. Rodents included the cotton rat, pocket mouse, pocket gopher, deer mouse, wood rat, and kangaroo rat. There was also one skunk. Birds, quail, duck, and pigeon, were infrequent. In one stomach there was 12% eggs of scaled quail ready to hatch. As for insects, there were grasshoppers, beetles, ants, and dragonflies. Vegetables included mesquite beans, cactus fruits, and persimmons.

A grey wolf—not naturally given to scavenging or to raids on domestic stock.

A further sample of 31 red wolf stomachs—18 from Texas, 9 from Oklahoma, 3 from Louisiana, 1 from Arkansas—contained 56% cotton-tail (*Sylvilagus*), and jack rabbits (*Lepus*); carrion, old cow and deer hide, 18%; deer 10% and grasshoppers, 7%. Other food items were turkey, moles, cotton-rat (*Sigmodon*), a sparrow, pine mouse (*Pitmys*), bugs, ground beetles, spiders and persimmons.

A sample of 8 grey wolf stomachs—6 from Michigan, 2 from Minnesota—contained carrion, 38%; deer, 25%; rabbit, 13%; red-backed mouse, 3%; great-horned owl, 5%; red-winged blackbird, 3%; grasshopper, 13%.

Ten grey wolf stomachs from Minnesota contained mostly deer, some carrion, and red-backed mouse. Ten stomachs from New Mexico contained livestock, 50%—cow, calf, swine; carrion 20%; deer, 20%; and rabbit, 10%.

These figures indicate clearly the situation of an animal whose natural food sources are scanty and which is eking out an existence on whatever it can acquire, including carrion which it does not like. In general, when domestic stock are attacked, this is done for the purpose of taking food and not from mischief or malice. It may well also occur because the domestic stock are more easily captured, even though wild prey is in adequate supply. Only with sheep do wolves occasionally indulge in reckless slaughter, as do dogs; there appears to be something about sheep which invites this kind of behaviour.

The picture of the wolf as an amiable country gentleman, living on the bounties of his estate, and taking his family for a winter holiday in the south, is a charming one. Alas! It is ecologically outdated, except for restricted areas in the far north. Wolves which survive in areas invaded by western man can hardly avoid supplementing their food supplies by raids on domestic stock, and farmers reasonably take the view that they are not raising the stock to feed wolves. Hence, the survival of the wolf in such areas is, to say the least, problematical. However, measures should and could be taken to ensure their survival, and stop their harassment in areas where they do no harm, such as the Barren Lands of northern Canada and Alaska, and in the far north of European and Asian Russia. Confinement of wolves in National Parks, as is seen in the Caucasus Reserve, is less likely to be successful because they require such enormous territories and because of their seasonally nomadic habits.

w—H

Social organisation and reproduction

The account given in the last chapter of wolves' feeding habits and their methods of acquiring food is unfortunately imprecise, and no doubt some of the statements made may well be challenged by some who have studied wolf behaviour. Precise scientific knowledge of wolf behaviour in different habitats, when different prey are hunted, and under a number of varying circumstances, is extremely difficult to obtain. A proportion of the food which wolves consume can plainly be acquired by single wolves on their own. They can gobble up small rodents, decoy ducks, catch fish, and eat berries all on their own, and they have been seen to do so. Occasionally, but only very occasionally, a lone wolf will tackle deer, caribou, moose, elk, or musk ox unaided by other wolves. Unless the prey animal is sick or maimed, a single wolf is physically unable to tackle it, and to do so is dangerous for the wolf's safety. Making use of their main sources of food, therefore, depends on the efficiency of their social organisation.

No clear picture of the social organisation of wolves has so far emerged. We have learned for certain what the wolf is not: he is not a voracious, ravening predator, who roams the plains and snowscapes in great packs, licking blood-stained lips, tearing down every living thing he can get hold of, and devouring innocent travellers. When nature, aided and abetted by man, contrives to destroy his habitat, he will seek other forms of prey or sustenance including domestic livestock. His attitude to man, in spite of persecution, is one of awe, and man is virtually never attacked either by lone wolves or by wolves in packs. Wolves do not wantonly kill their prey and indeed are unable to do so. They do not desecrate the herds on which they live, nor do they take the prime young breeding stock, but only as a rule the sick, the maimed, and the unfit. Indeed, their hunting methods are surprisingly unsuccessful; they travel great distances to find an animal they can seize, and even then a number of abortive attacks are usually made before they succeed.

A domestic scene—a she-wolf with two playful cubs.

This fact, which is well established, lends some support to the opinions expressed by some of the more recent observers of wolf behaviour that their hunting methods are by no means as well organised or as cunning as has been described in the last chapter. It is claimed that their methods are somewhat hit-and-miss and that they do not have the capacity to organise their hunts in the way that was previously supposed. Such ideas result from well-organised scientific surveys, such as those described by L. David Mech on the small wolf packs of Isle Royal in Lake Superior. However, such surveys are inevitably conducted on small groups of wolves which are hunting a single prey species, and only techniques adapted to the capture of this one prey can be studied. Such writers point to the imprecision of observations made by early hunters and to some of the more non-sensical statements which have been made. Nevertheless, the early hunters were actually trekking with the bison and so with their attendant wolves, and inevitably acquired a much broader perspective. It is impossible, therefore, to discount all that they said as being unscientific and unconfirmed, particularly since many of the conditions which they observed no longer exist. In order to obtain a perspective of the wolf in more natural conditions, when both wolves and prey were more numerous, it is essential to sift the earlier writings and to glean from them any information that may be of value. When one does this, one cannot dismiss the wolf as a rather blundering and haphazard hunter, as the more modern researchers on a more limited scale seem to suggest.

We may also recall that all those qualities we find in our domestic dogs were or are present in their ancestors, the wild-living wolf populations. For instance, the skill of a herd dog in controlling sheep and cattle is acquired from the parent wolves. We can therefore justifiably attribute to wolves the capacity to control and direct herds of wild animals in such a way as to make them vulnerable to attack. Furthermore, the herd dog learns readily to obey the command of the farmer by word of mouth or by whistle, and we therefore cannot dismiss the notion that wolves will obey the instructions of the pack leader given in some code that we do not know. Both wolves and domestic dogs can hear sounds of frequencies above and below those audible to the human ear and we do not possess the senses to judge of this.

We have, then, to build a composite picture acquired from all possible sources of information, treating each with due scepticism. The tales about wolves to be gleaned from mediaeval writings and earlier are so frankly prejudiced as to be of no value except in so far as they relate to historical fact dealing mostly with methods and laws for extermination. There is, however, much useful information to be acquired from Young and Goldman's excellent work on the *Wolves of North America*, in which the tales of early buffalo hunters and travellers in North America are related, though without much critical analysis. Much of the information given about wolves' organisation, habits, and hunting methods is confirmed in surprising detail by the accounts of Russian observers as related by such authors as Ognev.

Such observations are further confirmed by Farley Mowat in his interesting book *Never Cry Wolf*. David Mech dismisses Farley Mowat's work as being largely imaginary for reasons which are not clear. Mowat spent the best part of a year in the Canadian Arctic, encamped close by the den of a wolf family, and was able to study their comings and goings and their general habits for the whole of this period. He had evidently not studied the literature relating to wolf behaviour in advance of his assignment, and for this reason much of what occurred was unsuspected. His account appears to this writer for this reason unprejudiced. He also became friendly with a number of Eskimos, who knew the terrain and wolf habits well, including a shaman who was of the wolf clan and claimed that he could interpret wolf sounds and communications. In spite of the

A red wolf making a threat display, and also showing fear. The mouth is wide open, the fangs bared, the hairs erect along mane and back—at the same time he is cringing away with tail between his legs.

racy nature of his writing, Mowat is careful to distinguish between what he himself actually observed and what was related to him by his Eskimo friends. This, together with the concordance of his observations with those of the buffalo hunters and the Russian observers, inclines this writer to give credence to what he has recorded.

On the casual observer front, we can include also the observations of Lois Crisler, who recorded the experiences of herself and her husband when living in the Alaskan Arctic during the caribou migration north and south. The Crislers obtained wolf cubs from the Eskimos and maintained them as part of their ménage at their Arctic cabin. In her book *Arctic Wild*, she strikingly confirmed all that has been written of the gentle nature of wolves, of their capacity for love and friendship, and of their powers to afford mutual help and to communicate with each other. In her further work, *Domestic Wild*, she tells of her harrowing, but rewarding, experiences in attempting to keep some of the wolves she brought from Alaska at her home in north-west U.S.A.

Therefore, we do not discount what has been written in more popular works, and by those without scientific training as observers, but we have, I hope, used this material with discretion to make a composite story based both on observed facts and on deduction from such fact if supported by the more controversial literature. A great deal has been written on the wolf, and it has been brilliantly reviewed and added to his own long experience by David Mech in his book *The Wolf*. Other outstanding contributions on wolves are Murie's *The Wolves of Mount McKinley*, and *The World of the Wolf*, by R. J. Rutter and D. H. Pimlott. An entertaining story of the last surviving wolves, and of how they were trapped and exterminated in certain parts of U.S.A., is related by S. P. Young in his book *The Last of the Loners*.

With these remarks, let us approach wolf organisation in the knowledge that the subject is controversial and that some of the sources of information would be criticised by some wolf observers.

Wolf organisation is based on the pack, and the pack is based on the territory. Without a territory, there can be no pack, since wolves do not mate and breed unless a territory has been acquired. A territory can only be acquired when an existing one becomes vacant on the death of one or other of the pair which owns it, the extermination of the pack which was previously in occupation, or when, as has been observed in recent years in Finland, wolves move into new areas from which they were formerly absent. Once one of a pair of wolves has died or been killed, a surviving member usually remains celibate, and the territory can be taken over by another dominant male, who will acquire a mate from some adjoining pack, and will then start a family and a new pack of his own. Sometimes also a dominant male wolf of the pack will become uninterested in breeding and another male will take over his conjugal duties though the original wolf retains his leadership. This is an unusual situation which, however, apparently does sometimes occur. Immigration into new areas, as in the Finnish experience, is initially made solely by male wolves, maybe the outcasts from established packs in contiguous areas; if suitable territories are found, females are subsequently introduced and new packs on new territories are founded.

The foundation of a wolf pack, then, results from the monogamous mating of a single pair of wolves. The female will usually be two years old or more, but the male not less than three. A den is found

Cubs are born blind, like puppies born to domestic dogs, and the eyes open after ten or twelve days.

or dug and three to six cubs are born in the early spring, earlier in more southerly areas and later further north; an average date might be in March. At six months, the young wolves are ready to take their part in the hunting and to accompany their parents on the southerly trek. When they return towards the year's end, the process is repeated but the yearling cubs form part of the pack though they live in a separate den from the parents. In this way, together with wolves of 'uncle' and 'aunt' status, a full pack is produced which forms a composite hunting unit, most members of which are related and have familial bonds to each other; recognise and accept each other; and jealously preserve their territory from intruders. Packs are normally formed of six to ten wolves, but exceptionally may be more than this, as much as sixteen to twenty. When packs are large, they usually hunt together, but occasionally split up into groups of two or three. It has been observed that one wolf of the pack inclines to separate and to lead a somewhat solitary existence. It has been conjectured that this is the wolf at the bottom of the 'pecking order', or an old wolf whose teeth are worn and cannot materially assist in the hunting. Such lone wolves often follow the main pack at a distance, and it is supposed feed on the leavings after the main pack has satisfied its

The she-wolf's strength is greatly taxed by bearing and raising the litter—the poor condition of the mother is in contrast with the health of her little cubs.

When the cubs emerge from the den, there is a great deal of play, in which the mother takes part.

hunger. Such is the general organisation, but it is thought that there is no very rigid adherence to it, since on occasions it has been seen that two female wolves combine in a single den to rear their cubs. All members of the pack are very solicitous of the cubs, will help in guarding and feeding them, and in teaching them to hunt.

The territories occupied by wolf packs vary quite considerably, according to the type of terrain and the availability of food. The smallest territories occupied by packs are around ten square miles, but in tundra conditions territories are usually a hundred square miles or more. The numbers in the pack can never be allowed to exceed what the territory can support. When numbers become excessive, it is found that disease epidemics, particularly of distemper and rabies, occur, and a high death toll reduces the population. It is an inexorable law of nature, which man alone attempts to defy, that in all animal species excessive young are produced. It follows that, in times of stress when populations diminish, numbers are quickly re-established when conditions become more favourable. A wolf population that becomes depleted can thereby be quickly re-established and this is why control measures to reduce their numbers have so little success. It is also why the depredations of wolves on herds of caribou and other prey animals have so little effect on their actual numbers. However, other mechanisms and disease are at work to limit pack sizes. There is first a rule that wolves do not reproduce, unless or until they have acquired a territory. Secondly, through inborn endocrine influences, litter sizes become reduced as the size of the pack tends to become too great. By these means, pack size and territorial area are normally in adjustment with each other.

The breeding cycle starts when the wolves return to the den from the winter migration. The actual month of the year varies with the latitude, the cubs being born earlier in more southerly and warmer regions. In central Russia, for example, the onset of rut occurs in the middle of February, the younger wolves of the family having been driven off a month earlier. The adult males then become very watchful of their females and never leave them. The male precedes the female making a broad trail over the deep snow and turns continually to see that she is following. The paired wolves seek their dens in early spring, these varying in nature in different vegetational zones. 'Wolf trails' lead off from the dens, even through forest. The gestation period, as with domestic dogs, is 60–62 days, after which three to eight cubs are born. The cubs are born blind like puppies, and the eyes open after ten to twelve days. At three weeks, the cubs leave the den and romp and play like puppies. After a month they begin to feed on food regurgitated for them by their mother or some other member of the pack. The adult wolves then begin to bring whole small animals, at first dead then half alive, so that the cubs can begin their hunting experience. After a time, the cubs are led to water and at the end of the summer the whole family goes off together to hunt. At this time, the family is rejoined by the older cubs and the younger ones receive instruction in hunting techniques.

There is no substantial variation of this account of wolves' lives in accounts from North America, Russia, and elsewhere. Wolves couple like dogs, and it takes some twenty to thirty minutes before they can uncouple. At this time, the mated pair are in obvious danger and other members of the pack will stand guard and preserve them from molestation. The reason for this strange apparent anomaly of mating is difficult to discern. Mech believes that it is associated with the bonding ties, which keep the male and female so close to each other throughout life. Physical mating between the male and female wolves occurs but once a year and the prolongation of the act by coupling may well reinforce the bond produced by the act of copulation. Mech points out that close familial bonding is the basis which keeps the pack united. In wolf cubs, the capacity to form such bonds is confined only to the first two months of life, and in adults the physical and psychological stimulus of a prolonged physical mating may be necessary to produce it. When young wolf cubs are taken into captivity, they will only produce bonds with their captors if taken at a very young age. In captivity, oestrus in the female wolves lasts only some three to five days, after which the female rejects the male. It is, therefore, only for a very short period in the year that these important bonds can be forged. The cubs exchange their woolly puppy coat for a rough hairy one with the development of their teeth. There is then a gradual transition to the first winter's coat. and a complete change to the summer pelage at one year.

Wolves' dens are frequently enlarged fox earths. They may be thirty feet long and a narrow tunnel leads to the whelping chamber. The floor consists merely of dried earth, which is kept clean by the mother's eating the excreta of her cubs. The cubs are ungainly creatures like puppies, because of the disproportionate growth of their feet and limbs. Sometimes, dens are exchanged during the season possibly because they become infested with fleas. When the dens are abandoned for the season, the cubs being two-and-a-half to three months old, the family removes itself to 'loafing spots' where there is a cache of meat. When the den is abandoned, however, it may continue to the end of the season to be occupied by the previous year's cubs.

The lives of wolves may be said to centre round the family, whose members display a great degree of love and affection for each other. Although an adult wolf that is wounded is in risk of being torn to pieces and eaten, great concern is shown for the cubs. When a suckling mother is killed, her cubs will be removed to the den of another she-wolf and suckled and brought up with her litter. Desperate attempts are made, and risks run, to rescue a cub—or indeed an adult wolf—that has been caught in a trap, or taken into captivity. The story of the wolf's life is a strange one, and we may wonder at its superficial resemblance to that of man himself, in which the family is for most people the basis of a satisfactory social life. Though man and wolf have been exposed to similar ecological conditions, surviving and hunting in the bitterly cold open country of the Arctic tundra, both have had to develop into social animals; and both have developed similar bonds and ties within the family. Both species produce young with different abilities and qualities, adapted to performing different tasks within a single social organisation. The resemblance is striking.

Psychology and behaviour

When wolves from the same pack meet each other, even after a short separation, they greet each other with an exuberant display of love and affection. There is a great wagging of tails; they place their forepaws on each other's necks; rear on their hind legs, kiss and lick each other; and then they bound away and chase each other in a game of tag. Displays such as this are commonly seen when the male wolf returns to his mate after the night's hunt, and indeed at all times the two mated wolves indulge in displays of affection towards each other. Wolves reared from cubhood in captivity embarrassingly greet their master or mistress with the same signs of affection, in spite of the aversion of the human species to being licked all over the face. Play amongst the members of the wolf pack is a feature of the life of wolves. Once the cubs have emerged from the den, they play and romp so exhaustingly and for so long that eventually the dam gets tired and refuses to participate any longer; then frequently one of the 'uncles' or 'aunts' takes over and also plays until either he or the cubs are exhausted. Even adults chase each other around in games of tag in a way that is reminiscent of domestic dogs. Farley Mowat believes that wolves have a highly developed sense of humour and play practical jokes on each other and often tease each other.

When the pack leaves for the hunt at dusk, it invariably sets up a howling session. The howling of wolves is generally regarded as something awesome, to strike a chill into the hearts of those that hear it. To the wolves, it appears to be a kind of music, like perhaps a regimental march, to inspire them and put courage in their hearts. All the wolves of the pack howl in chorus, their heads thrown back and their mouths wide open, each adopting a different key. If two wolves of the pack are howling on the same note, one quickly changes, so that the different sounds together produce the sound which humans find so fearsome. The howl is started by one wolf only, but the other wolves of the pack quickly join in. The commonest

Within the hierarchy northern grey wolves show a great deal of love and affection for other members of the same pack. This is demonstrated in ways similar to those displayed by domestic dogs.

133

time is at the start of the hunt, but howls may be set up at any time during the day or night, seemingly for the pure joy of making music. When a pack sets up a howl, it is often answered by another pack in an adjoining territory and other packs around may also join in, so that the night around is made hideous—or beautiful according to point of view—by these eerie sounds. Hunters or students of wolf behaviour often set up howls imitating those of the wolves in order to elicit a response and to discover the whereabouts of wolf packs. The howl is easily imitated by the human voice, or it may be played on a tape recorder. When prey is located, a peculiar ceremonial takes place. The wolves of the pack yip and yap in an excited manner, tails are raised, and they all go into a huddle licking and endearing each other. They then set off in single file towards where the prey has been located; the dominant wolf is usually in the middle of the file and can be identified because he alone has his tail raised as an emblem of rank.

Temperamentally, wolves are very variable. Young and Goldman, in particular, draw attention in their writings to the great variation in intelligence, disposition, timidity, boldness, viciousness, strength and size, even amongst cubs from the same litter. These differences

Play is important for wolves, especially for the cubs. Stamina and courage are built up, and traits of dominance will begin to emerge in one or other even at this early stage.

All members of a pack will play and hunt together in apparent equality, but when wolves meet one another, opposite, the subordinate shows respect for the dominant by submissive behaviour.

become apparent even before the eyes are open. When raised in captivity, some are kindly and affectionate, others sulky and vicious and cannot be tamed. This spread of ability is comparable to that found in human beings, and is an essential feature of a highly organised group of animals that require a spread of abilities to obtain their prey and to live in the inhospitable Arctic terrain. Those wolves, destined to become dominant members and leaders of the pack, clearly show their qualities of leadership when they are still cubs, and exact obedience from their litter mates.

When wolves meet wolves from a neighbouring pack or ones that are strange to them, they indulge in behaviour so reminiscent of domestic dogs as to be ludicrous. Hackles rise, ears are cocked, the body is drawn to full height; then a cautious approach is made face to face with some growling; the tails are raised and there follows the nose-to-anus sniffing procedure, in which domestic dogs indulge. Having marked each other's scent, they break apart, make urine patches, sniff each other's urine, and then perhaps bound away in a frolic chasing each other. Unlike domestic dogs, these antics rarely if ever end in a fight between the two. If the one wolf has invaded the other's territory, the invader with signs of submission will slink away

without disputing the mastership of the territory owner. A subordinate wolf, even of the same pack, will approach the more dominant in a submissive manner, crouching low with the tail between the legs, and will often also roll over on his back exposing his belly. Meanwhile, the dominant, standing erect and proud, accepts the submission in a lordly manner and may condescend to lick and sniff his supplicant.

Our survey has given no indications of the evil desperate killer, so feared by our ancestors. Rather do we find an intelligent, lovable, and tolerant creature, whose family life and generous instincts put us to shame. In wolves, we find displayed the physical qualities that are spread through the many breeds of domestic dogs, combined with their great capacity for love, loyalty, and sacrifice. That modern man, with his inherent fear of these animals, should today attempt to domesticate wolves is unthinkable. A tame wolf would create panic in Magnolia Avenue, and people such as the Crislers, who have kept wolves tamed from cubhood even in remote areas, have been so beset with difficulties, that even they would not like to repeat the experience. If the wolves can get away, they love to roam sometimes for days on end, finding their livelihood by catching small game and rabbits, but also taking sheep and calves. Sooner or later they are shot by some indignant farmer and the experience is harrowing to the owner.

Yet our ancestors domesticated wolves, and the Eskimos still do. The wolves' great qualities were complementary to those of man. Man developed greater cunning, dexterity, and ability to organise; the wolves were superior in their senses, speed and stamina. Man was defenceless and forced to develop weapons; man had no defences against the cold and had to tame fire, and hunt for skins to clothe himself, as well as for food. Man had keen eyes but his sense of scent was deficient, and although his hearing was keen he was less able to discern the direction from which sounds came than were wolves. Wolves, on the other hand, could make greater use of the carcass after the kill. Man, with his weak tooth equipment, could use only the tenderer parts of the animals he killed, and required a fire with which to cook his meat and make it tender and palatable. So, a carcass killed by a human hand provided also food for the wolves, and even in historic times there was sharing.

Intelligence apart, the outstanding feature of the wolves is their amazing strength and stamina. They could in their hunting cover forty or fifty miles in a night, and still be fresh enough to make a kill at the end of it. If they failed to find prey, they could endure three to four days without feeding. When they killed they could gorge themselves with up to thirty pounds of meat, till they were 'meat drunk',

Opposite above, an injured wolf will tend to isolate himself from the pack until completely recovered. Below, grey wolves in the cold, wintry conditions which they have evolved to survive without difficulty.

in this respect resembling the Bushman peoples of South Africa. When on winter trek, wolf packs would consume every last particle of the kill. When in their home territory in the summer they are more frugal, hiding away meat and bones in caches to which they return, even as domestic dogs bury bones.

In hunting game, according to the Russian author Ognev, the sense of hearing is more important to wolves than the other senses. Prey animals are followed against the wind, not because the scent carries better but because they are heard better. This may, at first, surprise us from our knowledge of our own hunting dogs, one group of which hunts by sight (in the greyhound group), the other hunting by scent like foxhounds. Yet, fancy a dog lying by the fireside apparently asleep. Suddenly he stirs and cocks his ears. The family has heard nothing, but the faithful dog has heard the sounds of his master's car. More, he has distinguished that one car from all the other traffic on the road. So with wolves: the hearing is marvellously acute; they can hear sounds from afar and identify them, locating the direction of the sound with great accuracy. They can also hear sounds which are above and below the frequencies audible to the human ear. It is possibly by the use of such frequencies that wolf packs communicate with each other in such a way that man is unaware of it. Possibly also sounds of these frequencies are used by wolves in their system of telecommunication, which Farley Mowat believes them to possess as recounted to him by his friend the Eskimo shaman. This shaman, indeed, claimed that he, being of the wolf clan, could hear and interpret some of these sounds. This shaman did communicate to Mowat information about the movements of caribou and of Eskimo travellers which he had, so he said, acquired by interpretation of the lupine telegraph, and for which there seemed to be no other explanation.

Grey wolves on the snowy wastes; howling as in the upper photograph, is generally in chorus, possibly as a means of communication.

The sight of wolves is not binocular, because the eyes are set at the side of the head and cannot combine to focus on an object. Their sense of distance and relative size, therefore, is poor, and things are not seen in perspective. Moreover, the structures in the retina associated with colour vision are poorly developed, so that a visual picture is largely black and white or varying shades of grey. When a greyhound follows a hare by sight, it sees an object moving ahead at speed, which its other senses tell it is a hare; it cannot identify it as a hare by sight alone.

Even sight-hunting hounds use also the sense of smell, especially when locating prey. Like greyhounds, wolves will sometimes 'course' small animals they think they can catch; in this activity, all accounts suggest that they use the sight sense rather than scent. The use of scent in hunting may have come preponderant in wolves that became

v—J

adapted to mountainous or forested habitat such as the Tibetan wolf, which has been suggested as the ancestor of the scent-hunting hounds. Wolves do not recognise each other by sight but by scent, any more than dogs recognise other dogs or people by sight. Alone of all his household, Odysseus' old dog recognised him after twenty years of war and wandering when he returned home to Ithaca disguised as a beggar. Even his wife, Penelope, could not identify him until he revealed secrets of the bedchamber. Although the old dog, Argos, was nearly blind, he knew his master by his scent, in spite of the odour of his beggar's rags. The old dog, neglected and forlorn, rolled over and died contentedly.

Wolves' powers of picking up and identifying scents from afar no doubt resemble those of domestic dogs and are prodigious by human standards. Nostrils are elevated and the air is sniffed to pick up the scent messages carried on the light breeze. In a way dog and wolf live in a different world to men. It is a world of sound and smells, but seen as a blur; our world is identified chiefly by what we see, to a lesser extent by what we hear; smells are often repugnant and warn us to avoid things, not to investigate them.

Among wolves, voice communication seems to be used mostly at a distance. They do not bark as freely as domestic dogs to show embarrassment, or vexation, or as an invitation to a walk or a hunt. Greeting between individuals is more by posture and attitude. Tail wagging shows pleasure; depression of the tail submission. Facial expressions are used to express emotions. Snarling and baring of the teeth express displeasure or threat. A pleased wrinkling of the muzzle serves as a smile. Boredom or embarrassment is shown by a yawn. These gestures, which have all been described in wolves, are so obviously all so canine that readers would immediately recognise them. Voice communication is not easily understood or interpreted, partly because the wolves use sounds outside the limits of human perception. Furthermore, wolves in captivity are generally silent, except for a nightly howl, so that the sounds they use in the wild cannot be studied in captive wolves. A domestic dog's bark, with its many inflections, is most expressive as all dog lovers know. Yet wolves rarely bark, and they use an array of sounds, which have been described by various observers and which can undoubtedly carry a great range of meaning.

Ognev describes the wolf voice as a long howl, which is deeper in the males and shriller in the females and which ends in a bark. The howl of the yearlings is the most high-pitched. The family howls, occurring regularly at twilight and in the morning, often sound like the baying of dogs, but wolves never bay when hunting like hounds in full cry. Farley Mowat's account of the variety and range of wolf

Wolves, like dogs, yawn to demonstrate boredom or embarrassment. Yawning was originally a mechanism whereby muscles were stretched and lymphatic vessels compressed to ensure a flow of lymph after a period of inactivity.

noises describes howls, wails, quavers, whines, grunts, growls, yips, and barks, all of which might be recognised also in domestic dogs. A combination of these various noises could well give wolves powers of communication to cover a great range of different meanings. Undoubtedly, these express their emotions; they could also be used to convey information or instructions in the hunt. It has never, of course, been suggested that wolves have the capacity for abstract thought or for conveying abstract ideas, a quality undoubtedly possessed by man alone.

Wolves sleep always with their senses alert, and are easily aroused by strange sounds or smells. Sleep is taken in short naps of ten minutes or so, after which the animal rises to its legs, stretches, turns around, and settles down again. Most sleep is taken during the day and hunting usually takes place at night. However, the wolf could not be described as a nocturnal animal in the strict sense of the term. During the breeding season, females and the cubs are active during the daytime. The selection of day or night for rest is purely opportunist, in spite of the wolves' general regular habits.

Intelligence, as with man, is difficult to assess. Wolves' sagacity in hunting methods and in avoiding traps and poison baits is considerable, and evidently the result of learning. Wolves' ability to learn is attested by the education in hunting given to the cubs, and is evident from the greater mortality of cubs from man-made contrivances for their destruction than of adults. This circumstance, however, could also point to a failure of communication between adult and cub, a failure to warn the latter of dangers that lurk. The authors Young and Goldman refer to a belief amongst Eskimos that wolves can count up to seven, but not beyond. If a band of seven Eskimos is following a family of wolves, they will become disturbed if one or more leave the band to waylay them; if, however, the band is more than seven, say ten, they will not notice if the numbers are diminished above seven. That wolves organise their hunting to some degree is undoubted, but how they do this is unknown. It is also disputed, as we have seen, whether this is a rather crude, hit-and-miss process, or whether intelligent planning is involved. They plainly have the sort of intelligence possessed by a sheep-dog in the sense that they can herd an animal or small herd of animals, separating them from the main body and forcing them to go in a pre-determined direction. They also have the intelligence to adapt their hunting methods by a wide variety of stratagems to different situations. Wolves plainly do not regard domestic dogs as of their number. Male wolves will mate with bitches and she-wolves with dogs. In spite of this, they readily attack and eat dogs when they can catch them. Dogs too do not appear to have a sense of affinity with wolves, and are readily trained

One wolf is starting a howling session. The others appear not to be interested, but will probably feel a compulsion to join in.

to hunt or kill them. On the other hand, wolves will not attack other wolves unless one is badly wounded, when it is killed and eaten. Evidently, therefore, they detect some fundamental differences between themselves and dogs, even those that are most closely related to them. That they do not normally attack man would appear to indicate that they regard him as more akin to themselves than they do dogs. This is a very difficult feature of wolf behaviour to explain. Possibly domestic dogs have acquired some distinctive scent from the circumstances of their lives, which the wolves regard as alien.

In general, it may be supposed that wolves are endowed with all the abilities of domestic dogs, but in different degree; that man has selected dogs with certain properties, and thereby intensified certain of them in certain breeds, while damping down others. Even so, wolves evidently have a wide degree of genetic diversity, and some cubs are born with certain abilities better developed than others. It is this diversity which has enabled man to select their progeny for the characters he requires.

It is reasonable to infer that all the properties we find in our dogs are present in wolves, though more pronounced in some individuals than in others. This may help us to answer the burning question, what powers wolves have to cope with problems in a rational way instead of merely obeying the dictates of their senses. Most dog-lovers can give numerous examples, in which their pets have worked out problems successfully and thereby overcome difficulties. A wolf-cub at his first hunt will obey his first instinct to bound after the caribou in a hopeless attempt to catch it. He must learn the right way to approach and isolate the prey, and undoubtedly some degree of reasoning and intelligent thought is involved and he has the capacity to learn it. The wolf's brain, weight for weight, is one third larger on average than that of the domestic dog, and from this we would suppose a higher degree of intellectual development. One may suggest that, apart from the higher primates, the wolves are the most intelligent of terrestrial mammals. It is sad that this splendid creature should have become pitted against man in an age-long struggle for superiority.

The domestication of the wolf

There is no shade of doubt that domestic dogs in all their variety are descended from wolves. There are some who maintain that some dogs have jackal blood. For example, the well known Austrian animal behaviourist Konrad Lorenz in his inimitable way sees in some breeds of domestic dog jackal-like characteristics and in others wolf-like characteristics. He argues his case solely from traits of behaviour. Others find small differences in the structure of the teeth of wolves and jackals, differences which the author, after examination of a number of skulls of wolves, jackals, and domestic dogs, has failed to discern. The absence of these structures in domestic dogs, they argue, shows that dogs are descended solely from wolves. This, however, proves nothing, because the tooth features of the jackals, if they exist, may be a genetically subordinate characteristic and would thus disappear in the event of mixed ancestry. Since nobody appears to suggest that dogs are descended solely from jackals, the argument revolves around the possibility that at some time in the past jackals were crossed with wolf stock and have therefore contributed to the ancestry of the dog, some of whose characteristics or behavioural traits are due to this ancestry. Jackals can certainly mate with wolves and dogs; the resulting progeny are fertile and can themselves produce young. On the face of it, therefore, it would appear probable that jackals were at one time crossed with canine blood. Indeed, it would seem unlikely that those indefatigable experimenters in domestication and animal breeding, the Ancient Egyptians, did not experiment with such crosses.

It is more difficult to believe that such crosses, made so long ago, resulted in the fixation of any recognisable breed of dog, or that the jackal genes have not long ago been bred out. To maintain a hybrid wolf/jackal breed of domestic dog would require continual breeding back to the jackal; indeed the breed would be unlikely to maintain its

The wolf was, except perhaps for the reindeer, almost certainly the first animal to be domesticated by selective breeding for special purposes. The Assyrians bred hounds of mastiff type, used in war and hunting.

145

character unless this were done each generation. This is certain because the jackal has a pair of chromosomes more than wolf or dog; the f1 generation is likely, therefore, to possess an intermediate number of chromosomes. The f2 generation will then possess either the wolf complement of chromosomes ('karyosome') or the jackal; the intermediate condition cannot continue beyond the f1 generation. It is not known whether chromosome counts have been made on wolf/jackal or dog/jackal crosses. However, a similar situation exists when foals are born to mules. The mule possesses chromosomes intermediate in number between those of the ass and the horse. The progeny from mule matings are either horse or ass; they are not mules.

Another suggestion made by some students of the subject needs to be taken more seriously. Difficulty is seen in the derivation of dogs directly from wild wolf stock, and it is, therefore, postulated that at some time there existed a wild dog species, closely related to wolves, which became from natural causes partially man-dependent, and that it is from these that domestic dogs are descended. There is no evidence that this occurred, and if it did no reason to place the non-dependent groups of wolves in a separate species. Obviously, the first wolves to be domesticated would be those living nearest to human settlements. With the difficulties encountered over finding prey following the climatic change at the end of the Ice Age, no doubt such wolves were scavenging around human settlements. Once human communities at this same time were forced to give up the nomadic life and began to live in settlements, it is not difficult to suppose that wolf cubs were reared in these settlements. Indeed, the very habits of wolves reared in human society, as recounted for example by Lois Crisler, would be advantageous. Lois was driven near to distraction because her beloved wolves would somehow escape from time to time from any enclosure she made, over or digging under, and would disappear to hunt, inevitably slaying her neighbours' calves or other stock; unless shot or otherwise killed, they always returned. If early man's domestic, but *not domesticated*, wolves should disappear on hunting forays and man should share in the spoil, he would hardly count this a disadvantage.

The date at which wolves were first domesticated is usually placed in the Mesolithic, the difficult time when forests had displaced the tundra over such a wide area but before Neolithic times when man had adapted himself to the new conditions. Such a date would fit in with a supposed natural advantage to man and wolf in this new relationship. It is unlikely, indeed, that the wolf was domesticated in the true sense of the word before this date. True domestication means that the wolves were not only taken into captivity but also selectively

The only canine admitted
to the pantheon of Ancient
Egypt—Anubis, perhaps
jackal, perhaps wolf or dog.

bred for qualities advantageous to their captors. It would be difficult for nomads to do this, especially with an animal possessing such proclivities for straying and hunting on its own.

All the same two circumstances raise a doubt as to whether wolves were not being kept captive before Mesolithic times. First, it is contended that the Australian aborigines must have reached the Australian continent before the end of the Pleistocene, when the ice melted. After this time, there was a rise in the level of the sea and the continent became too isolated for them to cross to it in their frail canoes. Since they undoubtedly took the dingos with them, they must have held them captive at least earlier than 18,000 B.C. Furthermore, since they were in a Palaeolithic stage of culture and still were when the Australian continent was discovered, this is evidence that at least some Palaeolithic people already possessed captive animals closely akin to wolf stock. Fossil dingo remains, discovered recently, have

Early evidence of domestication is this skeleton, possibly of a dog of the mastiff group, recovered during Neolithic excavations at Windmill Hill, Wiltshire, England. It was probably a general purpose dog, used for herding and hunting.

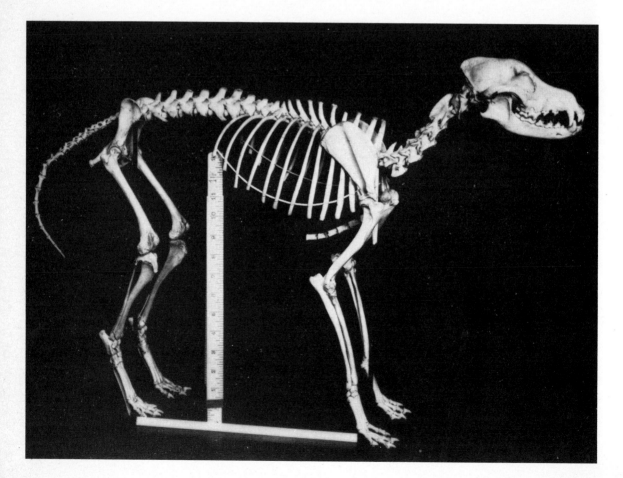

furthermore been carbon-dated to around 30,000 B.C. It would therefore appear that wolves were in the captivity of this group of the human race long before the end of the Pleistocene.

Nevertheless, there is no evidence that these peoples ever attempted to domesticate these animals, which are an ecotype of the Asian wolf (*Canis lupus pallipes*), and should probably be classified as wolves rather than dogs. Australian-type peoples are found to this day in isolated pockets along their migration routes. They are present in New Guinea, Indonesia, and in various parts of India as far as the north-west. In New Guinea, a partly domesticated form of the dingo exists in the so-called New Guinea singing dog, which is a small dingo with a specially melodious howl reproduced regularly at dusk. Although the Australian aborigines never attempted to domesticate the dingo, some efforts at this were made by their kinsmen living in New Guinea.

The second item of evidence which suggests that wolves had been made captive by man before the Mesolithic era comes from the far north. It is often disputed whether the first animal to be domesticated was the wolf or the reindeer. However, in neither case is true domestication the point at issue. In late Palaeolithic times, northern peoples were in the habit of herding the reindeer so that they could more easily kill or capture them for their needs. Latterly, at any rate, dogs were used to herd them and it is difficult to see how they could have been successfully herded without the help of dogs. On balance, therefore, one must suppose that these peoples had taken northern wolves into captivity and found that some at any rate had the ability to control reindeer herds. From then, they came eventually to breed selectively for this ability and so started the breeds of herd dogs which survive to this day. These people were not living in forested areas as were the Mesolithic peoples, but in the traditional tundra habitat. The wolf had, therefore, been taken into alliance with man, in conditions where the demands of climatic change were not forcing this on him. As to whether this occurred before the Ice Ages ended, and if so how long before, there is no evidence, but occur it did. The most probable explanation is that captive wolves were released to kill reindeer, the carcass being then retrieved. In the course of time, it would be discovered that some of the wolves could be trained to separate reindeer without killing them and would even obey vocal orders directing them where and how to direct the animals.

The second important use to which captive wolves were put was in drawing sledges, again appropriate to tundra rather than to forested areas. When and how wolves were first harnessed to sledges is quite unknown. Nor is it known when man first used sledges to pull loads across the ice and snow. To suppose that he did not use hurdles

The husky—these dogs are still the closest to the parent wolf.

for drawing loads of meat or carcasses across the snowscape in very early times is to underestimate his intelligence. Once he had wolves in his possession, it would be a rather obvious contrivance to tie one or more to the front of the sledge and urge them to pull it. To this day, wolves are occasionally included in sledge teams and work willingly and efficiently. In northern Russia and Greenland, where sophisticated sledge dogs, such as samoyeds and malamutes, have been bred, the huskies used by the Eskimos are closely akin to wolves and are bred back to them every few generations. Even in a more sophisticated country, such as Pakistan, dogs such as Alsatians (German shepherd dogs) are to this day back-crossed with wolves.

The beginnings of wolf domestication, therefore, certainly lie with peoples in a Palaeolithic culture and may have started much earlier than is generally supposed. Domestication of food animals in Near Eastern settlements came comparatively recently, not much earlier than 10,000 B.C. By this time, in more northerly areas wolf domestication had become quite sophisticated; already, different breeds are recognizable: miniature breeds, herd dogs, hunting dogs and so on. In the Near and Middle East, domestic dogs appear at around the same time or rather later than do food animals. The types of dogs they came to breed were in striking contrast to those of more northerly areas. Northerly peoples developed herd dogs, which could be trained to round up and corral animals, the ancestors of 'cattle and sheep dogs'.

The more southerly peoples developed 'shepherd dogs', dogs of great size and ferocity, which were used, not for rounding up animals, but to protect them from wolves. Although both groups are commonly called sheep-dogs, they are in fact fundamentally different. Once Near and Middle Eastern peoples realised that they needed dogs, they probably acquired them at first from stocks that were already domesticated, but the evidence suggests that they then took steps to breed them from newly acquired wolf ancestors, which would transmit the qualities they desired.

The extreme diversity of domestic dogs appears at first sight to be so bewildering as to make it impossible to classify them or attribute any definite ancestry from particular wolf groups. The great Linnaeus himself tried to give different breeds specific names, but abandoned the attempt and classed them all as *Canis familiaris*. The task is not, however, so difficult as appears at first sight, and domestic dogs can be divided into four groups, attributing to each an ancestry from a different ancestral wolf stock. Plainly, the four groups have been so interbred that the ancestry of some breeds is very mixed. Nevertheless, most breeds can be attributed to one group or other, and this classification has not been challenged. With certain groups or breeds, the attribution is sufficiently obvious to leave no doubt about the matter. The four groups are: 1 the dingo group; 2 the northern group; 3 the greyhound group; and 4 the mastiff group.

The dingo group

The true dingos are plainly captive or feral Asian wolves. They are smaller and slighter than *Canis lupus pallipes*, and their colour is yellowish instead of white and grey; they are thus an ecotype, which has diverged in response to the Australian habitat. They were taken

Domestication ranges from these dingos, which are not truly domesticated, to highly selected breeds like the Pekingese.

to Australia by the Aborigines and became feral. As feral animals, they show the same characteristics as do the Asian wolves, combining in packs to hunt in social groups. An offshoot of this group is the pariah dogs, found from the Indian sub-continent through the Middle and Near East into Egypt. The pariahs show certain characters of the tail and head, which show that they were at one time bred selectively. Possibly, they were the dogs originally bred in the Near East, before larger breeds were produced from alternative wolf stock; they were then discarded and became scavengers around human settlements and cities. They were the dogs which ate the body of Jezebel, and were evidently despised scavengers even at that time. The Ancient Egyptians, however, bred them, since they are depicted as one of the Egyptian breeds on tomb and temple walls. From them evidently arose the yellow dogs found throughout Africa, of which the basenji is one recognised breed.

Dogs of the dingo group account for some 50 per cent of the world's domestic dogs. They have also contributed to the ancestry of some important breeds by being crossed with dogs of other groups. They were the dogs of the Finno-Ugrian peoples, who migrated north from central Europe and settled in Finland and Lapland. In these areas, they were crossed with dogs of the northern group. The progeny produced dogs such as the elkhounds, which show some dingo/pariah characteristics in the conformation of the head and the curly tail. Another migration of dingo-group dogs took place through China and they have transmitted some of their characteristics to the samoyeds and chow chows. The ancestry of dogs of dingo type can, therefore, be directly traced to the Asian wolves and their derivation is not in doubt.

The northern group

There is equally no doubt as to the derivation of some of the dogs placed in the northern group. The most obvious are the huskies, which are clearly domesticated northern wolves (*Canis lupus*). The northern wolves are the ancestors also of the sheep dogs, such as the Alsatians and collies, though the collies are believed to have derived their slender muzzles and small 'stop' from admixture with saluki blood (greyhound group). The elkhounds are also dogs of the northern group, but with some admixture of dingo blood. From them we can also derive the terriers, and dogs such as the Maltese. Dogs of Old English sheepdog type appear to be of mixed ancestry, northern group and mastiff group. Here again, we have a direct line of descent which leaves no doubt as to the ancestry of the former members of the group.

Elkhounds belong basically to the northern group of dogs, which are derived from the grey wolf.

Shaggy dogs of Old English type were originally developed in the Russian steppes from 'shepherd' dogs of mastiff origin and the true 'sheep' dogs of collie origin.

Borzois, below, are dogs of greyhound type developed in southern Russia as wolfhounds.

The greyhound group

The greyhound group of dogs comprises the true greyhounds, the salukis, the borzois, the Afghans, the Irish wolfhounds and the Scottish deerhounds. That they are a homogeneous group, with properties quite separate from other groups of dogs, is not in doubt. They are also known as the 'sight-hunting hounds' to distinguish them from other hounds, which use the sense of smell to a greater extent. As a group, they are of great antiquity since they are depicted on Ancient Egyptian tombs and temples. As early as 1900 B.C., there were at least three breeds, recognizably greyhound or saluki. Their group characteristics clearly separate them from the other groups. Apart from their sight-hunting habits, they are of slim build with very deep chests and excel in speed and endurance. They have been widely distributed throughout Mediterranean countries from biblical times onwards. It is, however, difficult to attribute their ancestry to any existing sub-species of wolf, though a desert origin may be suspected. Amongst still existing groups only the desert Arabian wolf (*Canis lupus arabs*) can be suggested, although a larger form of this may at one time have existed in the western deserts of Egypt.

The mastiff group

The mastiff group comprises the mastiffs and bulldogs, the scent-hunting hounds such as the bloodhounds, foxhounds, etc, hunting dogs such as the retrievers, pointers, setters, and spaniels, and such dogs as the St Bernard, Pyrenean mountain dogs and so on. They are derived from the Molossians, famous in Graeco-Roman times, the enormous hunting mastiffs shown on Assyrian friezes, and from very large and fierce dogs, such as the Bunjara, which were present in India. They show group characteristics, which serve to identify a common lineage. They were clearly bred in response to the need for a very large and fierce dog for house and flock protection. If, as suggested above, they were independently developed from a separate ancestral source of wolves, they are the latest group of wolves to be domesticated. However, unlike the dingos and northern dogs, there is no obvious wolf group to which their ancestry can be certainly attributed. It appears likely that they were mountain wolves and their reliance on scent rather than sight in hunting suggests that they came from a forest habitat. Traditionally, ancestors of the Molossians came from India. The likely candidate is therefore the Tibetan mountain wolf (*Canis lupus chanco*), which may formerly have had a wider distribution into northern India or even through the mountainous regions of Persia into Anatolia.

Bulldogs are typically mastiff-type dogs, as evidenced by their conformation, coat, and other characteristics.

Opposite, the Asian wolf, smaller and lighter than the northern grey wolf.

From what has been said, it will be clear that our domestic dogs have been bred independently from at least two sub-species of wild wolves, and the evidence that there have been four sub-species, though circumstantial, is very strong. If it were not so, it might be doubted whether so great a range of domestic dog breeds could have been produced, since the four basic groups have been so widely inter-bred. Nevertheless, the main types of domestic dogs we know to-day, the miniature breeds, herd dogs, war dogs, hunting dogs, were already in existence many centuries B.C. Even such peculiar forms as the Pekingese are many centuries old. It is difficult to envisage such a dog as a miniature wolf, but in a sense that is what it is.

The point was made in an earlier chapter that, in selectively breeding dogs, man had introduced nothing that was not already there in the parent wolf stock. Nothing new has been created, though certain desired characters have been intensified by mating only those animals which are exceptionally endowed with them. When this is done, certain other qualities may be suppressed, so that no one all-purpose type of dog can be produced. Hence the necessity for the multifarious breeds. It is often said that the most intelligent dogs are mongrels, and indeed the mongrel may be the nearest possible approach to an all-purpose breed of dog. A mongrel possessed by the author in East Africa, part terrier and part goodness knows what, was an excellent hunting dog; he would flush and locate guinea fowl shot in thick country; he would drag a dead duck or a goose from a lake, and even course and run down a small duiker. However, he could not be taught to 'point' like a pointer, 'set' like a setter, or retrieve like a 'retriever'.

Some may say that this statement is an obvious absurdity. Look at the variation of size and colour in domestic dogs. Nothing like this exists in the parent wolf stock. Yet, size presents no problem. Each animal species has its large and pygmy forms, even elephants and hippopotamus, even man himself. Even in wolves, the size is very variable; there is a considerable size range in the northern wolf alone, and the difference between the largest northern wolves and the Arabian desert wolves is very great indeed. As regards colour, too, there is great variation from black to white even in the northern wolves, and a great range of reds and fawns in other species. The genetics of colour inheritance in all animals, including Canidae, are extremely complex and cannot be discussed here. Nevertheless, the genes for the colour diversities of domestic dogs undoubtedly exist in the ancestral wolves, so that by persistent breeding for certain colour phases all the varying colours and markings of domestic dogs can be produced.

Wolf cubs are playful and alert—it is thus that they learn much about the world around them.

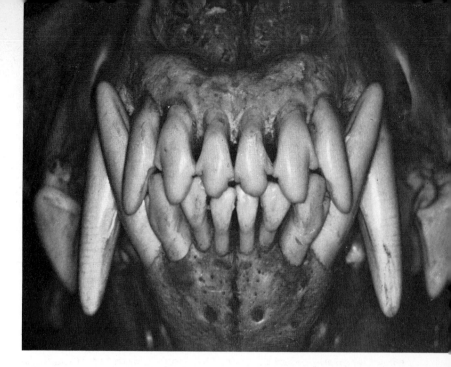

The extreme effects of domestication: a boxer (centre) and a Pekingese (bottom) compared with an Alsatian (top). In the lower two, the muzzles are fore-shortened to the point of deformity, with loss of some of the incisor teeth and deformation of the canines. The Alsatian shows typical wolf-like structure, but the teeth are weaker and more crowded.

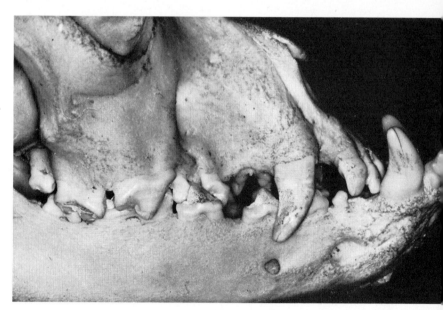

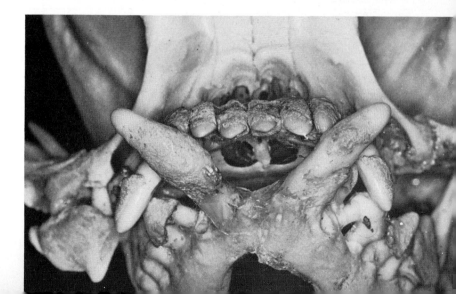

Amongst the four sub-species of wolves from which domestic dogs have been bred, there has undoubtedly been some 'genetic drift', and perhaps a small degree of gene mutation, giving rise to differences of habit and temperament, of size, colour, and conformation, and of adaptation to different climatic conditions. This has made it possible to breed for a greater range of qualities than would have been the case had only one wolf ecotype been used for selection. It is arguable that all our domestic animals, in which extreme variation is shown, are bred from diverse parent stocks, and that this is a precondition of success. It is certainly true of horses and possibly of cattle. Nevertheless the principle stands, that nothing is introduced by domestication that was not already present in the parent animals' genes.

This being so, some consideration of the properties of domestic dogs and the uses to which they are put can be helpful in understanding the range of abilities already present, though maybe mostly dormant, in the ancestral wolves.

Perhaps the most outstanding quality of the domestic dog is his love and loyalty to his master. The capacity for love and affection in the parent wolves has already been adequately illustrated. The dog also identifies himself with his master's property and family, and he takes on duties of his own accord, which may be unexpected and at times disconcerting. Once a Labrador retriever, the gentlest of creatures who had never bared a fang in anger, attacked a visitor in our garden, when he approached a grand-daughter's pram. This was the more surprising, since he was intensely jealous of the child, feeling himself supplanted, and the mother was being careful to keep him at a distance from her. The affectionate response of dogs, derived from their wolf ancestry, led to the desire for pet dogs, which could conveniently be introduced to the home. Even in Neolithic times, the first miniature dogs, allied to the Maltese, had been bred. In each of the four groups, miniature dogs, suitable for love or ornament, have been produced. Amongst the dingos, there are the New Guinea singing dogs, and the basenjis; amongst the northern dogs, there are the miniature terriers; amongst the greyhounds, the miniature Italian greyhound; amongst the mastiffs, there are the small spaniels, Pekingeses and so on. On the humanitarian front, one may mention the marvellous work done by dogs trained to lead the blind, which with unerring instinct will lead their protégés safely across crowded city streets, and the St Bernards which rescued travellers stranded in the snow.

At the other end of the scale, dogs are trained for brutal and dangerous purposes. Enormous mastiffs were used by the Assyrians and other Near Eastern peoples and wolfhounds by the Celts to

In the wolf's make-up are all the characteristics accentuated in domestic dogs by selective breeding, including a great capacity for affection of humans.

attack the enemy before the advancing infantry—the 'dogs of war'. As guards of property, some breeds of dogs are extremely dangerous and will kill a grown man. Wolfhounds will catch and kill wolves. Police dogs, such as Dobermans and Alsatians, not only show fierceness and courage but great sagacity also. The dog's keen scent can be used to smell out hidden drugs, or persons that have used them.

The herding capacity of sheep and herd dogs we have already noted as a property of the wolf ancestors, which has been brought to perfection by domestic breeding. Therefore, the uncanny precision with which the dog wheels the herds where required and rounds up stragglers need cause little surprise. More surprising is the response of the dog to the herdsman's vocal directions, from which it is difficult to believe that wolves in the wild do not respond to directions from the pack leader, controlling the segregation of the victim and the attack.

Hunting with packs of hounds was customary in classical times and earlier and is described by Xenophon. In these early days, also, dogs were used to locate and indicate the presence of game and freeze in a pointing or setting attitude. Again, that the descendants of wolves should locate game is not surprising. That they should be capable of learning restraint and discipline, when game has been located, may justly cause surprise, and may indicate a higher degree of pack discipline in wolves than some students of wolves are prepared to admit. If not exercised, the capacity was there.

One could continue to write at length of the purposes, good and bad, to which the wolves' descendants have been put. They draw sledges and carry loads; they do circus tricks; breeds such as the bulldogs have been bred for fighting, and the dogged adherence of the wolf to its prey has been intensified. They will carry the master's newspaper, walk on their hind legs, sacrifice their lives for their owners, track and run down criminals. The capacity for all these activities is present in the ancestral wolves.

Cy deuise autir maniere pour prendre les loups.

Wolf and man

In days gone by, one of the main purposes for which dogs or hounds were bred was the hunting of wolves. It seems anomalous that domesticated wolves should be used to hunt their wild cousins, and in a way distasteful. Nevertheless, with the object of 'setting a thief to catch a thief', there was no doubt sense in it, and before the era of the internal combustion engine there was little alternative except for destruction of the wolf's habitat or food supplies. However, as we shall see, hunting of wolves had little success beyond controlling their numbers, and extermination in countries such as England and Scotland was only achieved when the human population grew to such a level that the forests and mountains where the wolves were living were cleared for habitation or agriculture. But these attempts to control wolves by the use of hounds or dogs are of interest none the less. Three groups of dogs or hounds are involved in herd control, herd protection or the hunting of wolves.

In northern areas, where dogs were domesticated earlier than in the cradles of agriculture in the Near and Middle East, the emphasis was on the control of herds, no thought being given to their protection from wolves. Thus, there emerged the true sheep-dogs of collie type, whose abilities in the control of herds or flocks have never been excelled. The German shepherd dog, or Alsatian, was another breed developed in the north in early times; they have provided some protection for herds and flocks, but were not sufficiently robust to tackle a wolf. Nor indeed could dogs of the English sheep-dog type, originally developed in central Russia and Hungary; they were dogs of a specialised type, with shaggy coats and fringes over the eyes to protect them from snow. Their abilities again lay in herd control rather than protection, though they were of a size and temperament to protect themselves against wolves.

When these dogs were first bred, their owners probably had little need for herd protection. True domesticated animals had yet to reach them. They were herding the reindeer and hunting the animals

A mediaeval device for trapping wolves, certainly more humane than the barbarous devices such as steel traps and poisoned baits that have been tried in more modern times.

163

of the forest. The wolves did not threaten their livelihood, and there was no reason to hunt them, though the skin of a wolf in winter pelage could be removed for clothing. These people did, none the less, breed hunting dogs of the same type, such as the elkhound, and smaller dogs of this kind, such as the Norwegian buhund, were used for hunting puffins and other birds. Men thus had the capacity to breed dogs of a size and stamina to hunt and kill wolves, if they had the need to do so—but they simply did not want dogs of this type.

In the later Near and Middle Eastern settlements, the situation was entirely different. Cattle, sheep and goats had been brought into domestication and were very vulnerable to attacks by wolves. Furthermore, the wolves were living in habitats of forest and mountain, and were often hungry and needed to supplement their natural food. Thus, incursion on the herds and flocks, whether on lowland pasture or herded on the hills, became serious, and protection necess-

Wolves on prey—note the alert expression and the characteristic light eyes of the wolf, slightly started, features which distinguish them from domestic dogs.

ary. In these circumstances the great herd dogs of Molossian or mastiff type were developed from the Pyrenees, through Macedonia, Anatolia, Iran and northern India. They were very powerful animals indeed, such that a wolf would hesitate to tackle, since he might well come off worse in the encounter. Whereas the herd and shepherd dogs were bred from the northern wolves, there is good reason to believe that the herd-protection dogs of the southern peoples were derived from the mountain wolf strains. From them they also bred a great many hunting dogs, the ancestors of our scent-hunting hounds. They did not, however, breed from them wolfhounds, that is, hounds used specifically for hunting and destroying wolves. Possibly, in the mountainous terrain where these dogs were bred, the natural hunting of wolves was impractical. Actual wolfhounds were all bred from dogs of greyhound type, in other words they were sight-hunting; one would presume from this that wolves were hunted in open country, where the great speed and stamina of these hounds would give them an advantage.

The ancestors of the wolfhounds proper were of very ancient lineage. Various breeds of greyhounds and salukis are depicted on Ancient Egyptian tombs of the 12th dynasty (1400 B.C.), though these were short-coated and of typical greyhound type. Hounds of definite wolfhound type first appear with the Celts and were being used as dogs of war in the conquest of northern Greece in 273 B.C. These hounds were the undoubted ancestors of the Irish wolfhounds, the Scottish deerhounds, the borzois from southern Russia, and the Afghans. In response to climatic demands, they had become woolly-coated and were bred to be of large size. A Russian account of the methods by which borzois hunted wolves reads as follows:

> The perfect wolfhounds must run up to the wolf, collar him by the neck, just under the ear, and when the two animals roll over, the hound must never lose his hold, or the wolf would turn round and snap him through the leg. Three of these hounds hold the best wolf powerless. The men can dismount from their horses and muzzle a wolf and take him alive.

This account undoubtedly refers to the hunting of wolves in open country. There is, nevertheless, abundant evidence that wolfhounds were being used in mediaeval times in countries such as England, Ireland, Scotland and France, where the wolves lived in their woodland. Indeed, the author's family crest, in use in France and England at least as early as the 13th century, is a 'wolfhound, gored and blooded proper'. Wolfhounds were, however, greatly valued for the control of wolves, as is shown by the grants of land given by the English kings in return for packs of wolfhounds, and by Cromwell's prohibition of their export from Ireland. Certainly, the hound would be of little value in close country, and one must suppose that their main use was on heath and woodland, or that the wolves were flushed into open country. Their main value was in coursing animals, when their great speed and stamina would enable them to overtake the prey. The ancestry of wolfhounds from the salukis is not in doubt and significantly borzoi pups are born with short coats, their shaggy pelage appearing only in adult life.

Wolfhounds had certainly been bred by the Celts by a very early date. In Roman times they were called 'Scottici Canes'; at that time the *Scotti* lived in Ireland. In 391 B.C. the Roman Consul Quintus Aurelius Symmachus, being short of animals for the Games, was driven to exhibit Irish wolfhounds. They did, however, cause as much sensation as if he had exhibited animals from the wild. The Scottish deerhounds were derived from Irish wolfhounds taken to Scotland in early Norman times. These same hounds were also well known in England up to the 16th century, where they were known as wire-haired British greyhounds.

It seems clear that wolves were first admitted to human settlements because they were useful allies in herding and hunting, and it is ironic that the domesticated wolves should have come to be used in the control of wolves themselves. It may be conjectured from the known habits of wolves that it was the wolves who first began to frequent human settlements to share in what meat was going in difficult times, rather than that man deliberately sought and captured the wolves. Domestication of wolves seems to have taken place at a time of great difficulty for the human race, because of climatic change. While the northern races of man were developing the earliest forms of stock husbandry, by herding and domesticating the reindeer, the more southerly invented agriculture. Thus, in response to a drastic change of climate, man embarked on a new way of life which was to alter the whole course of earth ecology, and lead incidentally to a new relationship with the wolf stock which remained wild. The wolves, for their part, sought to adapt themselves to new environments of forest and mountain. However, food sources were insufficient for an animal of such roving habits and they started to raid human settlements especially in winter, preying on the livestock and scaring the people. Stories of their depredations were no doubt exaggerated, and many crimes laid at their door which they did not commit. We can easily see how these eerie, silent animals, with their eyes glowing by night, would arouse a superstitious fear in the hearts of people no longer used to their presence near their settlements. Furthermore, the inroads they made on their stock, both that in the palisades and that herded on the hills, were undoubtedly serious.

The wolf, unlike many other animals, has not been a greatly favoured subject for artists—this flask, with wolf-shaped handle, dates from about 1450 B.C.

Already in pre-Roman times wolves were regarded as verminous pests to be exterminated. Nevertheless, perhaps some relic of an early affection persisted in ancient legend, as in that of Romulus and Remus, founders of Rome, who were supposed to have been suckled by a she-wolf. There was, also, obvious admiration of the wolf's strength and sagacity, as is shown by the custom of ancient Nordic kings of adopting wolf names, such as Beowulf or Beadowulf (the war-wolf), Berthewolf, Cynewolf, Wulfstan, Wulfred, Wolfwig, and Ceowulf (wolfish kings).

It is evident from the records and experiences already quoted that North American wolves, at any rate, unless affected with rabies, avoid or ignore man. They do not wantonly attack him, even under extreme provocation. Present-day Russian records appear to support this; nevertheless, from Saxon times onwards, whatever the truth of the matter, it was evidently believed that wolves were a deadly menace from which no human being was safe. Earlier than Saxon times there are virtually no records which reveal the situation; nevertheless, the Celtic peoples bred hounds of the Irish wolfhound type, which they used in warfare as well, but the purpose of which was originally the hunting of wolves. From Saxon times onwards there is abundant literature, which is extensively quoted by Millais (1904) in his *The Mammals of Great Britain and Ireland*. From these records we may follow the story of the association of wolf and man in the time that has elapsed since the Ice Age to the wolf's extermination in so many countries in comparatively recent times.

In Great Britain and Ireland, wolves were very numerous from the lower Pleistocene onwards. Relics have been found in at least thirteen counties of England and Wales, Berkshire, Derbyshire, Devonshire, Glamorgan, Gloucestershire, Kent, Essex, Norfolk, Oxford, Somerset, Sussex, Wiltshire, and Yorkshire. It is recorded that an early Celtic king, Mempricius or Memprys, who was a great wolf hunter, was eaten by wolves in 980 B.C.; in fact, he was probably assassinated and his body thrown to the wolves. Wolves were still abundant when the Romans came and they were then being actively hunted. The Anglo-Saxons also hunted them with avidity and Alfred the Great had the reputation of being a particularly keen wolf hunter. At this time, wolves were so abundant, and believed so exceptionally dangerous, that January was set apart especially for hunting them and was called *Wolfmonat* or wolf month. An outlaw was known as *Wolvesheofod* or wolf's head, that is there was a price on his head alive or dead as with a wolf. It was in the reign of King Athelstan that refuges called Spittals were erected in wild parts, so that travellers could find protection from wolves; the name still survives, as in Spittal Farm in Yorkshire.

Romulus and Remus, founders of Rome, being 'suckled by a she-wolf'. It has been suggested that the babies' foster parents, Faustulus and his wife Acca Larentia, were wolf-cult people and regarded as wolves or were-wolves by their neighbours.

The early English kings used to levy taxes on the Welsh kings, but in order that the numbers of wolves should be reduced they accepted payment in the form of dead wolves. Criminals, too, were permitted to pay for their crimes in the form of wolves' tongues. In 1016, the Danish King Canute excluded foxes and wolves from the laws of venery, thus classing them as vermin.

Wolves remained abundant in England until the time of Henry VI, being found notably in the New Forest, the Forest of Savernake, the Forest of Richmond in Yorkshire, Blackburn and Bowland Forests in Lancashire, Sherwood Forest in Nottinghamshire, the Forest of the Peak in Derbyshire, and the Forest of Riddlesdale in Northumberland. All these forests were much more extensive than now, and it is to be noted that the wolves were confined to forest habitats, alien to their natural way of life. Kings Richard I, John, and Henry III all made grants of land to individuals who undertook to keep the numbers of wolves in check. In the reign of Edward I, tenants in the county of Northampton held their lands on condition that they kept hounds hunting wolves, and wolfhounds were common in many parts of the country through the reigns of all the Edwards, Richard II, Henry IV, Henry V, and Henry VI. After this, wolves became more scarce.

How much of the vendetta against wolves was really intended to limit their numbers is uncertain. In the book of St Albans (1486), the wolf is included amongst beasts of the chase; the season for hunting it was between December 25th and March 25th. These dates would include the cubbing season, when wolves would be most vulnerable. The restriction of the hunting season might indicate a half-hearted attempt at conservation. By this time, the extent of the forests had diminished greatly and the numbers of hunting squires had increased proportionately; the wolf gave exceptionally good sport and so, as with foxes today, it may well have been wished to control wolf numbers rather than to exterminate them. However, it was not the bounties or the hunting squires which rang the death knell of the wolves, but the restriction of the forested habitat which gave them shelter. The same occurred in Scotland as we shall see. Wolves are supposed to have become extinct in England between 1485 and 1509 during the reign of King Henry VII, though some may have lingered on in the forests of Lancashire and the wolds of Yorkshire for a time after this. Many place names commemorate the presence of wolves, such as Wolmer or Wolvermere, Wolfscote in Derbyshire, Wolfhamcote in Warwickshire, Wolferlowe in Hereford, Wolf's Castle in Pembroke, Wolfpits in Radnor, Wolfscrag in Sussex, and Wolfenden and Wolfstones in Lancashire.

In Scotland the fourth King of the Scots, Dormadilla or Dovadil, who reigned in the second century B.C., enacted hunting laws and decreed that whoever killed a wolf should receive an ox. Wolves were hunted with great vigour, because they killed so many cattle which were the sole wealth of the people. Dovadil's successor, Elderus, who was contemporary with Julius Caesar, was especially fond of wolf hunts. Besides being very numerous in Scotland itself, wolves were also found in great numbers in the border country between England and Scotland where they were regarded as vermin. In the reign of James I, there was a plague of wolves, coinciding with the time when their numbers were being drastically reduced in England. One wonders whether perhaps some of them had not been driven out of England. James enacted laws for statutory hunts, which took place between St Mark's Day (April 25th) and Lammas (August 1st), when the cubs were young. These same laws were re-enacted by James II. Even so, the numbers of wolves in the great highland forests reached alarming proportions from time to time. Numbers diminished during the reigns of James III and IV, but they were again on the increase under James V.

In those days there was a continuous cover of Scotch fir and birch over the greater part of Perthshire, Argyllshire, Inverness, Ross and Cromarty, from which the wolves would emerge to harry the cattle

Sheep being penned for their own security. During the Middle Ages there was a very real need to protect sheep and other livestock, even dogs, from wolves.

The Big Bad Wolf of legend, poised to devour a little girl. Strangely, in fact they virtually never attack human beings, unless suffering from rabies.

and then retreat. The wolf plague reached its height during the reign of Mary, Queen of Scots, and the animals are said to have spread unexampled devastation. When hungry, they ransacked the churchyards unearthing newly buried corpses. In Sutherland, these depredations became so serious that the dead were taken to nearby rocky islands for burial. In 1563, Mary, Queen of Scots, attended a wolf hunt by hounds. In the reign of James VI (1577), the county of Strathnavern became infested with enormous numbers of very fierce wolves, which set upon the cattle with great ferocity, and it was made compulsory to hunt them three times a year.

They were eventually eliminated from Scotland by destruction of their habitat, as in England. Great tracts of forest were burnt and as a result their numbers were greatly reduced. Regrettably, the forests

170

themselves did not recover either. All the same, wolves survived in the wilds of Braemar into the 17th century and were found in Sutherland until 1621. It is usually said that they were extinct by 1684, but a few stragglers seem to have survived until between 1690 and 1700. Tradition even has it that the last wolf was killed in 1848.

In Ireland also wolves were very numerous in the Pleistocene, preying on the very large reindeer that lived there. They are said in historic times to have had their cubs as early as December, because of the very mild climate. They were very numerous between the years 1357 and 1387. They were traditionally hunted by the famous Irish wolfhounds. Many ordinances appear in the state papers of the Irish kings providing for their destruction, because of the damage they did to the herds. Under English rule, a bill was introduced into the Irish Parliament in 1611 for the destruction of wolves, but it was never promulgated because of the fear by the ruling power that wolf-hunting assemblages would be an excuse for insurrection. So,

the wolves preyed on the herds unmolested until the time of Cromwell, who as usual took a strong hand and forbade the export of 'wolf-dogges' in 1652. Legislation was also passed giving bounties for wolves destroyed; these were generous, if not lavish for the time—£6 for a bitch, £5 for a dog, £2 for a cub shifting by itself, and 10/- for a suckling cub. However, they were still numerous in 1669. The last wolf was certainly dead by 1821. As in England and Scotland, the decline of the wolves occurred only when the human population spread so widely as to reduce their habitat.

The story of the wolf in the British Isles and Ireland is typical of that in other European countries, where these animals have been exterminated, and indeed of what is happening in North America. It is the story of an animal in an unsuitable habitat, hungry because the prey in the habitat is inadequate and forced to raid on the forest confines stealing domestic stock. It is the story of ecological change following climatic change. In the newer ways of life, those old allies, wolf and man, have become ecologically incompatible. The wolf appears to retain a respect for human beings, and is reluctant to attack them. Not so man, who now fears and abominates the wolf and does all in his power to destroy him. Alas, he fails to recognise in the wolf's descendant, whom he has domesticated, the great virtues and lovable characters of the ancestral wolf. If wolves must become extinct in some areas, let us yet give what honour is due to him and preserve him where we can. The old traditions of this gentle creature's savagery and ferocity linger on, and man's hand is against him, even when he does no harm. There are still enormous regions of the world, in America and Russia, where he can be left unmolested; let him so remain.

Opposite above, a herd of buffalo, or bison, at their watering place. The size and strength of these animals are quite evident here: it is the pack organisation of wolves which enables them to hunt them with success. Below, members of a pack of grey wolves after the kill: the animal is an elk.

Religion, myths and magic

The late Sir Winston Churchill once said that there was no value in history, except for the lessons it taught for the future. So what place have ancient beliefs and mythology in a serious study about wolves? Throughout this book we have seen how man's outlook on wolves has radically changed, since the world's ecology and topography were drastically altered at the end of the last Ice Age, beginning some 20,000 years ago. This was long before recorded history, and most tales, myths and records of wolves merely reflect the changed outlook which accompanied the ecological changes. Hence, any clues to the former relationship of man with his fellow predator of the tundras must be sought in myths and legends, which may have survived from very early times. These, too, have become so greatly distorted that to unravel a coherent story presents great difficulty. However, research on the subject does seem to be rewarding, as we shall see.

There is clear evidence that in late Palaeolithic times, at any rate, the lives of our ancestors were to some extent ruled by mysticism. This is revealed in the paintings on their cave settlements in France and Spain. The well known picture of the 'horned god' serves to connect the rites of early man with witch cults, which survived to the Middle Ages, even possibly to the present day. Most of the paintings, however, are concerned with hunting, and depict the prey animals —bison, deer, horse, and appear to represent a propitiation of some god, possibly the animal itself, for success in the hunting. From much more recent evidence we know that there was a mystical association between the hunter and the hunted animal. The Hairy Ainus, a primitive Caucasian people living in the northern Japanese islands, provide the best known example. These people's religion is a form of animism combined with ancestor worship, but they also worship bears which they hunt and eat. When a bear is killed, the subsequent feast includes an elaborate ceremony for the propitiation of the bear's spirit, designed to convince the victim that honour is

Timber wolves, from Canada.

being done to him of benefit to his spiritual life. If this were omitted, other bears in future would withhold themselves and hunting would end in failure. The Scythians of old worshipped horses, which had from time immemorial been hunted for food by their ancestors and which had latterly been domesticated for riding and drawing chariots. The horse cult probably arose in Palaeolithic times, since the Solu-trean hunters had covered the walls of their caves with well drawn representations of horses, some with feathered darts sticking in their flanks.

Red Riding Hood—the wolf of folk legend is always the Big Bad Wolf, crafty and ravening for human blood.

Thus, primitive man came to worship those animals that were of use to him. Horses were worshipped by the more northern peoples, but significantly not by more southerly peoples, although the latter had acquired and were using horses by the 5th century B.C. One may

suppose, therefore, that the deification of animals of importance to the tribe occurred much earlier than this. Amongst more southerly peoples, the chief cult animal was the bull, which was widely revered and worshipped, showing it to be of special importance in the economy. This outlook is perhaps not so strange, when it is re-membered that at the end of the Ice Age man was faced with virtual extinction unless he found a new way of life, and this he did by domestication of crops and animals. It followed that his crops became associated with mystical ceremonies featuring the birth and death of the year and his animals were regarded with superstitious awe as a supernatural benefactor. The latter, indeed, followed naturally on the belief that the hunted creature was in some sense co-operative and had to be propitiated.

We have seen that the fellowship of man with wolf, which we have inferred, existed among the more northerly peoples who were hunting on the snowscapes of the tundra. Traces of it would not be expected amongst more southerly folk, who led a different kind of life, except, as with the early Greeks, where they were immigrants from the north. The wolf was undoubtedly useful to man. He was the ancestor of his domestic dogs, and his pelt was valued to provide warm clothing and furs. One might expect, therefore, that the wolf would have achieved some degree of deification if only in a minor capacity. We do indeed find the wolf included in Scandinavian mythology, as would be expected, but regrettably not in a favourable light. One Celtic deity was Cernunnos, traditionally seated between a wolf and a stag, probably a relic of the old hunting/propitiation mythology. The Scandinavian deities, or rather demons, were Fenris-wolf and Garm, the former a wolf of evil disposition and the latter an enormous dog, indicating an origin of the legend subsequent to wolf domestication.

Fenriswolf was descended from the giant Ymir, a spirit of evil. At the same time, there lived a perfect man, Bure, descended from a cow, and he had three sons, Odin, Vile and Ve (Spirit, Will and Holiness). The three brothers slew the giant Ymir, but so much blood flowed from him that the entire race of giants was drowned with the exception of Bergelmir and his wife, who escaped in a boat. They produced numerous offspring, with whom Thor and the other gods carried on constant war. At length a truce was arranged between the gods and one son Loki, the representation of all evil, of giant race, fair but of bad disposition. However, the gods found his strength and cunning of value and he becomes the foster brother of Odin, although he was continually plotting for their downfall. Loki became the father of three terrible children in Jotunheim, the land of the giants. These were the Fenriswolf, the Midgard serpent, and

Hel, goddess of death. Aware of trouble brewing for them, the gods took steps for their disposal. The Fenriswolf was bound on a barren island and a sword was placed in his open mouth, but to do this the god Tyr had to sacrifice his right hand. However, the tables were turned on the gods by the wicked Loki, who encompassed the death of the wisest and best of the gods, Balder. Balder was the son of Odin and Frigga, but suffered from terrible dreams, indicating that his life was in danger. As a result, Frigga took an oath of all things that they would do no harm to Balder, but she overlooked the mistletoe. So successful was this treatment that the gods amused themselves by

throwing missiles at Balder, who suffered no harm. However, Loki induced the blind god Hoder to throw a bough of mistletoe at his brother, and a twig pierced his heart.

With Balder's death, the powers of evil were let loose on the earth. There are continuous winters with no summer. The sun and moon are swallowed by giants, who pursue them in the guise of wolves, and the heavens are stained with blood. Loki emerges as the leader of the hosts of Hel. The Fenriswolf is released, opens his enormous mouth, and fire flashes from his mouth and nostrils. The Midgard serpent at his side vomits forth floods of venom that fill the air and

In demon role, the wolf appears in Norse mythology. However, he appears here as an amiable attendant, with the stag, of the Celtic god Cernunnos.

waters. Thus the forces of evil become arrayed for the final fray with the gods. Odin himself faces the Fenriswolf. In the last stages, the dog Garm breaks loose, having been for ages chained in the Gnipa cave. He is the most terrible monster of all, and attacks Tyr who had given his right hand to chain the Fenriswolf. Garm and Tyr kill each other. The Fenriswolf with his enormous mouth swallows Odin, but Vidor, Odin's son, advances to avenge his father. He places his foot on the wolf's lower jaw, seizing the other with his hand, and rends him to death, aided by the magical shoes he wears. Finally, the world is consumed by fire and sinks beneath the waters. A new and better world subsequently arises.

This story, though necessary to recount, does little to advance our search for evidence of a time when man and wolf lived in respectful communion. It plainly dates from a time when metal was in use as is shown by the reference to the sword placed in the Fenriswolf's mouth. Wolves are arrayed with the powers of evil and associated with the giants, who fight the gods. Possibly, it represents the race memory of some war between immigrant peoples and aborigines who used dogs and wolves in their battles, and with whom the invading peoples sometimes made common cause.

Apart from this doubtful association with the forces of evil in their struggle against the good, the wolf achieved deification in a minor way in Ancient Egypt. He was deified by the inhabitants of the city of Lycopolis in lower Egypt—not, one feels, a very high honour. The name of the city, being Greek, implies that it was a city of Ptolemaic times founded under Greek rule in the years preceding the Christian era. Every city in Ancient Egypt adopted some animal as its 'beast-god', the beast representing the god Ammon in Upper Egypt and Ra in Lower Egypt. Once a year at the god's festival, the city's beast would be killed and its skin used to clothe the image of the god, which would be buried in a sacred tomb. At this later date, the wolf is more likely to have been adopted in respect for the ancient custom than for any belief in his divinity. The Ancient Egyptians possessed an insatiable curiosity about animals, and brought into captivity any animals they could lay their hands on, and which would survive. When the animals died, their bodies were embalmed and they were laid in tombs in stone sarcophagi. Even small rodents were accorded this respect. In Ptolemaic times, too, great processions were arranged in Alexandria on civic occasions, and every conceivable type of animal life was paraded in enormous numbers. Amongst the animals paraded were wolves. Whether wolves still existed in Egypt at that time cannot be said, but they did exist in nearby countries. These would be either Asian wolves (*Canis lupus pallipes*) or Arabian wolves (*Canis lupus arabs*). So, the wolf that took part in these processions and that deified at Lycopolis are likely to have been one of these two species. More convincing evidence of wolf-worship in ancient times will be discussed in relation to the were-wolf cult; otherwise, one must record with regret that the wolf in myth and fable is invariably regarded as evil, a verdict of history which as we have seen is unjust. However, let us seek those tenuous clues from a more ancient past which may show him in a better light. For example there is evidence to link him with the ancient 'totem' system.

The totem system is still widespread amongst the native peoples of sub-Saharan Africa and elsewhere. Children, when born, become members of a totem clan inherited from the mother or father, depending on whether inheritance is matriarchal or patriarchal. The totem clans have nothing whatever to do with the tribe into which the child is born. Each clan is signified by an animal, which may be a bushbuck or a crocodile, a lion or a hippopotamus or something else. Membership of the clan involves certain duties and certain restrictions. A clan member will not kill or eat the flesh of the totem animal even when starving. Members also have duties of hospitality and mutual

A papyrus depicting the Ancient Egyptian jackal god weighing the souls of the dead.

assistance to other members of the same clan, even though they belong to a different tribe and speak a different language. There thus exists over wide areas of Africa a form of healthy freemasonry, whose obligations are mandatory and strictly observed.

It would appear that this ancient system must have survived from the days when Palaeolithic man roamed the earth as a nomadic hunter in small bands. Marriage within the band would be tabu for the very good reason that such marriages between closely related persons would sooner or later result in the perpetuation of genetic defects. Thus exogamy, or marriage outside the family circle, was essential and it would even be necessary to avoid marriage with closely related persons in neighbouring bands. A totem system would enable recognition of related persons, ensure respect for mutual obligations, and lead to the avoidance of inter-marriage between related persons.

That the wolf was—and still is—a totem animal is shown by Farley Mowat's account of his friend, the Eskimo shaman, Ootek. The shaman system is not confined to the Eskimos, but prevails also throughout northern Siberia and among the Amerindians. The wolf, therefore, is still a totem animal, presumably over a wide area of the northern world. In the past, he must have played a much bigger role over a wider area than today. Ootek claimed that, as a child of four, he had been left by his father for twenty-four hours in a wolf's den. If this is true it is evidence of the intimate relationship which existed between the totem animal and clan members. James Frazer, in the *Golden Bough*, also refers to the wolf as being a widespread totem animal amongst the North American Indians. Farley Mowat's shaman, Ootek, was, however, insistent that a young baby could not survive amongst wolves, not because the wolves would not wish it to do so, but because it would not be able to suckle the she-wolf. At the age of four to five years, when Ootek was left with the wolves, the child could survive at any rate for a certain length of time.

The totem origin also gives the most rational explanation of the were-wolf legends. James Frazer describes the custom amongst the North American Indians of dressing up in the skins and masks of the totem animal, and imitating that animal's behaviour. Were-wolves were thus no figments of imagination or legends; they actually existed in the sense of wolf clan members disguising themselves as their clan animals. Such behaviour is manifested to this day by members of leopard clans in Africa. They don the skins and masks of leopards, and in this disguise will attack people with metal talons constructed to look like leopard's claws. Thus were-leopards still exist. However, let us study the origins and significance of the were-wolf story.

A were-wolf is a man having the power by magical or supernatural means to turn himself into a wolf. The technical term is lycanthropy, and it is used for the power generally of certain humans to transform themselves into carnivorous animals although the word-derivation from the Greek indicates wolves only. In Scandinavia, men were supposed to turn themselves into bears, in Africa into leopards, in Asia into tigers or hyaenas, and in South America into jaguars. Lycanthropy persists to this day in many parts of sub-Saharan Africa, as we have seen, and in Abyssinia, in India and Nepal, in the Chindwin Valley, and in Java and Sumatra. The propensity today is believed to be hereditary, a belief which is undoubtedly correct if today it is a survival of the totem system. Virgil referred in the Eclogues to the practice, and supposed the transformation to be the result of taking drugs.

Were-wolves were very prevalent in mediaeval Europe, and especially in France during the late 16th century. In that country, around 1573, there was a plague of were-wolves, the best known being a certain Giles Garnier. They were known as *loups-garous*; however, two men convicted by the courts as being were-wolves were adjudged to be insane. In Britain and Scandinavia, lycanthropy was associated with outlawry; some outlaws became 'bereserkers'; they wore wolf or bearskin garments and were subject to paroxysmal, bestial fury. It has been suggested that in Europe were-wolves were once associated with orgiastic societies which indulged in cannibalism; these

There was for centuries a firm belief in the evil and dangerous nature of wolves, and in the existence of were-wolves, even among churchmen.

may have been related to witch fertility cults, as is the case with the
West African leopard cults. A similar society, the members of which
were known as Kwakiuth, formerly existed on Vancouver Island;
these people wore wolf masks and gorged on raw human flesh.

In theory, the soul of the were-wolf was projected into the body of
some beast, while his own body was cataleptic. Wounds inflicted on
the beast's body were projected on the cataleptic body of the were-
wolf. In an animistic society, in perpetual awe of the magic of witch
doctors, such an explanation would appear entirely feasible, and this
enabled the were-wolves to terrorise the community and no doubt
extract wealth and other advantages for themselves. This could
hardly have happened in early times, when the community was
familiar with the habits of wolves. Lycanthropy would appear,
therefore, to be a depraved survival of the totem system, and one
wonders how many atrocities ascribed to wolves in mediaeval times
were in fact committed by its devotees.

A connection between lycanthropy and totemism was first suggested by Sir William Ridgway in his *Early Age of Greece*, and
early Greek legends lend support to this idea. The question is
discussed at length by Montagu Summers in *The Werewolf*. The
great centre of were-wolfism in Dorian times was Arcadia, and
Pausanias in his Eighth Book of the *Description of Greece* (c. 166 A.D.)
speaks of were-wolves still being existent there. He wrote (quoted
from Summers):

> The Arcadians say that Pelasgus was the first man that lived in
> this land . . . Pelasgus' son Lycaon outdid his father in the
> ingenuity of the schemes he projected. For he built a city
> Lycosura on Mount Lycaean, he gave to Zeus the surname of
> Lycaean and he founded the Lycaean games . . . In my opinion
> Lycaon was contemporary with Cecrops, King of Athens . . .
> Cecrops was the first to give to Zeus the surname of Supreme,
> and he refused to sacrifice anything that had life . . . Whereas
> Lycaon brought a human babe to the altar of Lycaean Zeus,
> and sacrificed it, and poured out the blood on the altar; and
> they say that immediately after the sacrifice he was turned into
> a wolf. For my own part I believe the tale: it has been handed
> down among the Arcadians from antiquity, and probability is
> in its favour . . . They say that from the time of Lycaon down-
> wards a man has always been turned into a wolf at the sacrifice
> of Lycaean Zeus, but that the transformation is not for life; for
> if, while he is a wolf, he abstains from human flesh, in the ninth
> year afterwards he changes back into a man, but if he has
> tasted human flesh he remains a beast for ever.

Mount Lycaeus was the sacred peak of Arcady, and Lycosura was about five miles away; it was excavated in 1889–95. The remains of the Temple of Zeus were found there—as Summers says, surely one of the most haunted places on earth. Ridgway suggested that the Lycaean Zeus may have arisen from some Semitic Baal imported from the groves of Syria. Nevertheless, the use of the word 'Lycaon', the Greek for wolf, is significant, and establishes the connection of the people of Arcadia with the wolf cult. Furthermore, it strongly suggests a totemic origin, as described above.

Pausanias' account appears from other authors to have been incomplete. Zeus himself, it will be recalled, was born in Crete, the son of Chronos and Rhea. Chronos was in the habit of killing his sons at birth and eating them. When Zeus was born, his mother descended to the depths of a deep and eerie cave in the mountains, where the birth took place and the child was saved, since Chronos could not find him. The cave is still shown to visitors, who like to brave its slimy depths, where water trickles and stalactites grow. According to Apollodoros in his *Bibliotheca*, Lycaon had many wives and was the

An 18th-century 'monster' —evidence of the place held by wolves and the like in the popular imagination.

Were-wolfism is perhaps a race-memory of the time when the ancient totem system operated—people during festivals would dress up as their totem animal and imitate its gestures.

father of fifty sons, who were impious and proud above all other men. Father Zeus visited their palaces, and in mockery they slew a child and mixed the entrails with the savoury mess served up for the guest. Zeus in anger overturned the table and blasted Lycaon and his sons with his thunderbolt. Only Nuktinos, the youngest, was spared at the behest of old Mother Earth. However, perhaps the fault was not altogether on Lycaon's side, because according to another story Zeus seduced Lycaon's daughter, Callisto, and Arcas was born. Arcas was, however, sacrificed by Lycaon, who was turned into a wolf and his sons killed by the thunderbolts.

Ridgway commenting on these stories wrote: 'It is possible that the story of the transformation of some of those present (i.e. at the Zeus sacrifice) into a wolf may have arisen from the circumstance that as the medicine men of modern totem clans often get themselves up like their totem animal, so the priest who officiated at the Lycaean rite may have arrayed himself in a wolfskin.' Another author, Mons. G. Fougères, gives three possible explanations for the rites which took place on Mount Lycaeus, one being that the cult was that of a totem; the wolf-god being the primitive deity of the aborigines of Arcadia, and the human sacrifices the cannibalistic feasts of a tribe of wolf men.

Apart from Arcadia, the worship of Zeus was associated neither with wolves nor with human sacrifice, lending support to the theory that Zeus Lycaeus was in fact a representation of the Syrian Baal. The wolf, however, is closely associated with the worship of the god Apollo, to whom in early days human sacrifice was offered at Leukas and in Cyprus. In Homer's time, the Argive Dorians worshipped Apollo Lykaos. Leto in her birth pangs, then in the form of a she-wolf, was led by wolves to the Isle of Delos, or as some say to the River Xanthos in Lycia, where she gave birth to Apollo, called by Pandarus in the Iliad 'Son of the She-Wolf'. Sometimes, the god adopted the wolf shape. The wolf was sacrificed to Apollo in Argos, being both the familiar animal and the sacrificial victim. At Delphi, it was said that the wolf was worshipped, and it was in the guise of a wolf that the god first pronounced his oracles. The Athenians, too, held the wolf in honour, and anybody who killed a wolf was required to pay for its burial. When Athens was infested by wolves, sacrifice was made to Apollo at the site of the Lyceum (note the recurrence of the Greek word 'Lykaos' for wolf) and the smell of the sacrifice drove the wolves away. It is also suggested that the Attic hero, Lukos, whose statue as a wolf stood near the law courts, was in fact a form of Apollo.

The she-wolf with Romulus and Remus, founders of Rome.

A 19th-century illustration of a 'wolf-charmer,' a notion found in France even in the last century, and thought to have developed from the were-wolf idea.

There is no doubt, therefore, that the were-wolf cult entered into the worship of Zeus in Arcadia and of Apollo in many parts of the ancient world. It cannot be seriously doubted either that we see here the link between the ancient totem system and the were-wolf superstitions of later days. Herodotus describes a similar situation in the tribe of the Neuri who dwelt in Scythia. The Neuri were sorcerers as was well known both by the Scythians and by Greek settlers in Scythian country. Each year, every Neurian became a wolf for a few days, and then resumed his original form. It is worth while in this context to consider the tale of Romulus and Remus.

Romulus was the legendary founder of Rome, the son of Mars by Rhea Silvia, daughter of Numitor, King of Alba Longa. He was exposed in the wild at birth with his twin brother, Remus, by his great uncle, Amulius, who had usurped the throne. The twins were suckled by a wolf and brought up by a peasant named Faustulus, and his wife Acca Larentia. He founded Rome in 753 B.C., but quarrelled with Remus, whom he slew. In 716, he was carried to heaven in a chariot of Mars, and was worshipped as the god Quirinus. It is generally accepted today that in most historical legends there is some grain of truth. However, it is not possible—as we have already seen—that the twin babies could indeed have been suckled by a she-. wolf. What, then, is the truth of the story, or is it pure myth? The most probable suggestion made is that Faustulus and Acca Larentia were wolf-cult people and regarded as wolves or were-wolves by their neighbours. The twins could indeed have been, at a later age, left overnight in a wolf-den, as Farley Mowat's shaman, Ootek, claimed had happened to him.

Were-wolf legends from all parts of the world have been collected by Elliot O'Donnell, and Summers has discussed the phenomenon with detailed reference in a learned and philosophical way. By mediaeval times, and indeed much earlier, these accounts are so overlaid with fantasy, and so mixed with rites of witchcraft and vampirism, that the origins and significance of the cult cannot be unravelled. The facts of importance to our argument emerge. First, the fact of were-wolfism was never called in question. It occurred, and the only difficulty lay in explaining it. Even learned divines of the Church accepted the fact and mostly attributed it to possession by demons. The argument swayed around whether the human actually became a wolf or dressed in a wolf's skin and adopted the behaviour of a wolf attacking flocks and humans, impelled by a lust for blood. Were-wolves, when accused before the courts, readily admitted their offence and evidently believed that they were at times transformed into wolves. As with witchcraft, it appears that these persons were smeared with drugs and swallowed potions which induced hallucinatory states, and some were found to possess wolf-skins which could be worn. The second point of importance which emerges concerns the use of skins. It was established that some were-wolves dressed themselves in wolf skins, the interior of which was smeared with unguents. However, this practice was gradually abandoned and the body alone was smeared. However, it was common practice for a girdle of wolf skin or even of other animal skin to be worn, thus preserving the semblance of dressing for the part at a time when whole skins may have been difficult to obtain and the significance had been forgotten.

The last were-wolf episode occurred in England around the year 1887; the creature was seen by the wife of an Oxford don beside a lake in the remote hills of Merioneth. The don was a great fisherman and he and his wife were staying in a remote area by the lake. The professor had found a huge canine skull, which he brought to the house. That same night his wife saw the hideous mask of a wolf with human eyes. The skull was thrown into the depths of the lake, when the trouble ceased.

Stories and legends thus lead back from the latter part of the 19th century to times long before history was recorded. Can we link these legends with the folk-lore of peoples living in close association with wolves in the Arctic hunting grounds? Are they relics of a time when wolf and man were associates and not antagonists? The myths of Ancient Greece and the association of the wolf with Zeus and Apollo suggest so. The matter could, no doubt, be clarified further by a study of the totem system and of wolf-lore amongst the Eskimos and other northern peoples.

The northern grey wolf.

The wolf in retrospect

From what has been discovered of the life of wolves, the moral is clear that proper studies and surveys of animals are essential if we are to understand the animal kingdom. Probably never have there been so many misconceptions about one species as there have been about wolves. It is understandable how myths about them should have arisen in countries where they have long since been extinct. Wolves were clearly a serious menace in countries such as Britain, Scotland and Ireland because of the depredations they made on livestock, which constituted an important part of the wealth of the people. One can hardly blame the people for pitiless behaviour towards the poor wolf which, like man, had lost is natural environment and was confined to a forest habitat unable to supply sufficient food, and forcing him to seek sustenance outside.

Nevertheless, in more northern countries reliable information about wolves' way of life and behaviour could readily have been obtained in recent times from those people, such as Eskimos, Lapps, and Samoyeds, who still lived in the same terrain and in apparent amity with them. The stories of the old buffalo-hunters of North America, in spite of their evident exaggerations, should also have led scientists to check the reliability of the old wives' tales. Belatedly, this has been happening and competent surveys of wolves in natural habitats have established their true nature and ways of living. Some fascinating information has now been obtained, much of it relevant to studies of human ecology.

When wolves first occupied the Ice Age habitats of Europe, Asia and America, they were naturally adapted to the terrain in which they lived, and they suited the ecological scene as predators of the large herds of grazing animals which found in these areas a good source of living. Such predators were, if anything, beneficial to the prey species rather than otherwise. The wolves themselves were well fed

April in the homeland of the wolf; this is the dwarf-willow-birch tundra in the interior of Alaska.

and lived out a normal life span in health and enjoyment as was their nature. Man, on the other hand, was an intruder on this scene, ill-adapted to the climate, though endowed with methods of hunting and survival hitherto unsurpassed in the animal kingdom. His intrusion is likely to have been the result of population pressures in his natural habitat far to the south, in Africa. In these new areas, he was deprived of some important items of diet such as fruit, which would provide vitamin C, and evidently of sources of vitamin D which in sunnier climates he no doubt acquired by exposure of his skin to the ultra-violet rays of sunlight. And so we find that the expectation of life of early Palaeolithic human races, such as the Neanderthal, was far short of modern expectations even in under-developed countries. There is, moreover, evidence of bone disease in fossil skeletons that have been recovered, which may have been the result of lack of either vitamins C or D.

Man's hunting methods were destructive; he trapped, corralled or drove animals to their deaths over precipices, far in excess of his requirements. This was probably advantageous to the wolves, who would eat the excess that the human bands did not require. Man was hunting animals, even wolves, not only for food but also for their skins, essential for warm clothing to protect him against the bitter Arctic climate.

Man, therefore, did not fit the ecological scene. Although, in early days, he seems to have been in some sort of partnership with the wolves leading eventually to domestication of the dog, his activities were destructive and did not contribute to ecological well-being. However, his numbers were small; he roamed the open country in small bands, and the overall effect was probably of little significance. He may well have nearly exterminated the horse stocks after the end of the Ice Age, but it is extremely doubtful whether he had any hand in exterminating the mammoths.

This was to change, when the Ice Age ended. Forests spread, and man was not only incapable of finding a satisfactory livelihood in forested country, he had a superstitious fear of forests and trees and hesitated to penetrate them. Following a period of uncertainty in Mesolithic times, his reaction to climatic change and to the alteration of the habitat was drastic and sure. He began to remove the forests he disliked; he started to grow his own crops and to raise his own livestock instead of hunting. In this way, he changed from a mere ecological misfit into a manipulator of the ecology. In some areas, he was and is reasonably successful; in others, such as the marginal grazing lands of the Sahara, the Sind desert and the dust bowls of North America, he has done near irreparable damage. Although a misfit, man was at least coming into conformity; but he then did himself a great deal of damage by projecting himself into an artificial milieu which he is now beginning to understand but which hitherto has been beyond him.

It is reasonable to hope that problems of urban living, of proper land control and food production are beginning to be understood and that the most pressing of them may be overcome within a reasonable period of time. Many problems have been or are being solved, such as the control of disease, the nurture of the young, and the ways in which people need to be fed to live healthy, adequate lives. In another sense, man's problems are only beginning to be tackled, chiefly those of the psychological adequacy of the environment in which he lives. We live in a world of increasing violence, of social unrest, and of hospitals half-filled with mental patients showing symptoms of withdrawal from an environment with which they feel inadequate to cope. In these spheres, a study of an uninhibited animal such as the wolf, which has evolved in harmonious relationship with its habitat, can teach useful lessons.

There are three aspects of wolf behaviour, which man has abandoned or tends to abandon in his own social relationships, and which are of paramount importance to race cohesion. The first of these is the territorial instinct; the second is the social unity of the wolf clan or family; and the third, related to this, is the methods by which the social bonds of the family are created and consolidated.

The rare red wolf of North America on the prowl for some small game.

As we have seen, no wolves form breeding pairs or social units, until a territory has in some way been acquired. Although there are other means of population control, this custom has a powerful effect in preventing wolf numbers rising to a level at which food supplies are inadequate; if population pressures tend to show themselves; changes of endocrine mechanisms or the toll of disease correct the situation. How different is this from the situations which have arisen among human beings in the last 10,000 years ? Man's numbers have increased so much that serious problems of malnutrition, epidemic diseases, and widespread misery have been created. New lands have been discovered and colonised, only to be affected by these problems in their turn. The world's resources have been exploited in such a way that the ecology has been damaged and the future of the human race itself has been put in jeopardy. We have flouted nature's primary and most important laws so that within the foreseeable future, or even now, the world's food resources cannot support the world population. Man must find some means to overcome this problem, if he is to survive.

The northern grey wolf of Europe—*Canis lupus* is still an important species in northern Europe and a large part of Asia.

From the social and familial organisation of wolves too, man can also learn some lessons. We have seen how wolves, faced with the problem of hunting much larger animals than themselves, necessarily had to set up a social organisation with a division of labour in the hunting and minding of the cubs, and that this required the provision of differing abilities among the different members of the pack. This, we have also shown, can be done best in a monogamous system where the qualities of many males are transmitted to the offspring. It could not so easily occur in a polygamous system, as with horses, in which a single powerful stallion gathers a herd of up to fifty mares and imprints his own stamp on all the young of his breeding. Man, when he entered the Arctic wastes, was already a socially organised predator and had been faced with similar problems. Human society also is primarily monogamous, although exceptions of course do occur, usually for economic reasons. In his case, an even greater range of abilities was necessary and this requirement has steadily increased during the years of civilisation. His nearest relatives, the chimpanzees, do not have a monogamous familial system, since the females when in oestrus are covered by many of the males of the troop, but the chimpanzees merely forage for vegetable foods in bands and, beyond the usual dominant/subordinate system, little social organisation is necessary. Wolves and man, therefore, share the same form of social organisation, developed for similar reasons, which is based on the family and family cohesion.

However, it is not only between the parents that social ties are important. It is the wolf family that forms the hunting pack, and it is on their cohesion that success in obtaining their food is achieved. Although some members of the pack are destined to be leaders and others subordinates, this ranking is accepted, and all members of the family show great cohesion and affection for each other. In human relationships too, there is usually a strong link between members of a single family. It is worthwhile for us humans to think again about these matters and to study the system in its origins as still revealed by communities such as those of wolves. Moreover, wolves virtually never fight amongst each other, in fact they never indulge in warfare between contiguous packs with the object of acquiring territory. It is likely that the human nomadic bands of the Pleistocene also had a mutual respect for each other's territories and did not fight each other to gain advantage. Indeed, it is only in the late Neolithic times that we find evidence of human settlements being fortified to give protection against assaults and invasion.

The ways in which these familial bonds are formed can also be studied in wolves and these can also teach lessons relevant to human behaviour. We have shown that the young wolf cubs form their bonding ties with their parents, with other members of the litter, and with other members of the pack during the first two months of their existence. When more than two months old, there is resistance to bonding and this ensures that the bonds are confined to the family and are not formed with members of other packs with whom the young wolves may meet when they leave their territory. It may be suggested that the human familial bonds are also formed during the pre-pubertal period of life, and this would explain the mysterious sense of family attachment which can even override dislike. This does not explain, however, how the close marital bonds of mated male and

A fine head of a 'buffalo wolf'.

female wolves are formed, and it is here that the suggestion of L. David Mech as to the purpose of coupling in wolves is of importance. Here again there is a similarity between wolf and human behaviour, which is worthy of remark. In human relationships, it is evident that the sexual act has a far greater significance than merely for the propagation of children. Sometimes following a period of experiment and promiscuity, the human male and female under most circumstances mate monogamously and copulate regularly and frequently, thus forging the marital bonds which are of such importance to the family. For each child born, a single couple will copulate many hundreds of times, giving to each other enjoyment and a sense of being one in a partnership. Whereas, however, the human female is at most times ready to mate, this is not the case with wolves, the females coming on heat but once a year and then for only a very short space of time. For this reason, Mech, as we have seen, attaches importance to the prolongation of the sexual act which is ensured by the prolonged and physiological process of coupling and uncoupling. How proof could be found that this is the source of monogamous bonding between male and female wolf is difficult to see, but the argument seems logical. Nature, or should we say evolution, has therefore provided both wolf and man with mechanisms by which firm bonds are created between the mated sexes and between the members of the family group.

This book ends in Victorian fashion with a chapter pointing to moral conclusions. This was not initially intended, but as the material unfolded itself the parallels between wolf and human behaviour appeared so striking that it was felt necessary to outline their possible significance in studies of human ecology. Indeed, man of today is deeply disturbed by the dangers inherent in his distorted behaviour patterns. Modern thought is leading us to study the behaviour patterns of less advanced and more uninhibited species in the hope that these can show us some way in which tragedy can be averted. It is a pleasure to dedicate this work to that nature's gentleman, the wolf.

Bibliography

BARTRAM, W. *The Travels of William Bartram.* New York, 1928.

BEDDARD, F. E. *Mammalia.* London and New York, 1902.

BILLINGS, 'Natural history of the wolf (*Canis Lupus*) and its varieties.' *Canad. Nat. and Geol.*, **1**(3), 209–15.

BROWN, D. *Wild Alaska.* New York, 1972.

CAMBRENSIS, G. *Historical Works* (1185/6, rev. and ed. by T. Wright). London, 1863.

CAMDEN, W. *Britannia.* 1586, trans. from Latin, London, 1637.

CAMPION, E. *A Historie of Ireland written in the Year 1571.* Dublin, 1633.

CARAS, R. *The Custer Wolf: Biography of a Renegade.* London, 1966.

CHAMBERS, R. *The History of Scotland from the Earliest Period to the Present Time* (2 vols.). London, 1832.

CLUTTON-BROCK, J. In *Science in Archaeology* ed. D. Brothwell and E. Higgs. London, 1971.

COWIE, I. *The Company of Adventurers; a Narrative of Seven Years of the Hudson Bay Company During 1867–1874 on the Great Buffalo Plains.* Toronto, 1913.

CRISLER, L. *Arctic Wild.* New York, 1968.

CRISLER, L. *Captive Wild.* New York, 1969.

FIENNES, R. and A. *The Natural History of the Dog.* London and New York, 1968/1969.

FITTIS, R. *Sports and Pastimes of Scotland.* Paisley, 1891.

FRASER, J. *The Golden Bough* (abridged ed.). London, 1950.

GRAY, A. P. *Mammalian Hybrids* (Tech. Comm. no. 10, Commonwealth Bureau of Animal Breeding and Genetics). Edinburgh, 1954.

HARRISON, D. L. *The Mammals of Arabia.* London, 1968.

HARTING, D. L. *British Animals Extinct in Historic Times.* London, 1880.

HOAGLAND, E. 'A mountain with a wolf on it stands a little taller.' *Sports Illustrated.* **40**, 74–86.

INNES, C. *Scotland in the Middle Ages.* Edinburgh, 1860.

JERDON, J. C. *The Mammals of India.* London, 1874.

JOSSELYN, J. *New England Rarities Discovered.* London and Boston, 1672.

LORENZ, K. *Man Meets Dog.* London, 1965.

LYDEKKER, R. *The Great and Small Game of India, Burma and Tibet.* London, 1900.

MANWOOD, J. *A Treatise and Discourse of the Lawes of the Forrest.* London, 1595.

MECH, L. D. *The Wolf: The Ecology and Behaviour of an Endangered Species.* New York, 1970.

MILLAIS, J. G. *The Mammals of Great Britain and Ireland.* London, 1904.

MIVART, ST. G. J. *Dogs, Jackals, Wolves and Foxes: Monograph of the Canidae.* London, 1890.

MOWAT, F. *Never Cry Wolf.* New York, 1963.

MURIE, A. *The Wolves of Mount McKinley* (U.S. National Park Service, Dept of the Interior, Fauna Series No. 5). 1944.

O'DONNELL, E. *Werewolves.* London, 1912.

OGNEV, S. I. *Mammals of Eastern Europe and Northern Asia*, vol. II. Jerusalem, Israel Program for Scientific Trans., 1962.

PINKERTON, J. *History of Scotland.* London, 1797.

PRATER, S. H. *The Book of Indian Animals*, 1965.

RIDGWAY, SIR W. *Early Age of Greece*, vol. II, p. 475. 1931.

RUTTER, R. J. and PIMLOTT, D. H. *The World of the Wolf*. Philadelphia, 1968.

SELYE, H. *The Physiology and Pathology of Exposure to Stress*. Montreal, 1950.

STRELKOV, A. A. *The Mammals of the Caucasus*. Jerusalem, Israel Program for Scientific Trans., 1967.

STRUTT, J. *Sports and Pastimes of the Peoples of England*. London, 1810.

SUMMERS, M. *The Werewolf*. London, 1933.

TOPSELL, E. *The Historie of Four-Footed Beastes*. London, 1607.

TOWNSEND, J. K. *Narrative of a Journey Across the Rocky Mountains to the Columbia River*, p. 118. Philadelphia, 1839.

TURBERVILLE, G. *Booke of Hunting* (1575). Oxford, 1908.

WINGE, H. *The Interrelationships of the Mammalian Genera*. Copenhagen, 1941-2.

YOUNG, S. P. *The Last of the Loners*. New York, 1970.

YOUNG, S. P. and GOLDMAN, E. A. *The Wolves of North America*. Washington, 1944.

ZEUNER, F. E. *A History of Domesticated Animals*. New York, 1964.

Picture acknowledgements

Colour

Wildlife Unlimited, photographs by Tom McHugh, supplied by Photo Researchers Inc., N.Y.C.: 33, 51 bottom, 137 top, 137 bottom, 138 top, 138 bottom, 173 bottom, 191. Photo Researchers Inc., N.Y.C.: Charlie Ott 34, 192; Tom McHugh 85; Russ Kinne 156, 173 top; Karl H. and Stephen Maslowski 174. Natural History Photographic Agency, Westerham: B. Hawkes 51 top; E. Hanumantha Rao A.F.I.A.P. 155. Pitch, Paris: Binois 52; P. Lefebvre 86. Cactus Clyde Productions, Maringouin, Louisiana: C. C. Lockwood 103, 104.

Black & white

Photo Researchers Inc., N.Y.C.: Karl H. Maslowski 10, 91, 108, 127, 132; Russ Kinne 12, 66, 119, 122, 128, 129, 134, 164; Don Carl Steffen 42 bottom; Tom McHugh 46–47, 68, 72, 75 top, 83 top; Charlie Ott 48–49; John Ebeling 55; Jerry L. Hout 112; F. B. Grunzweig 113; Todd Webb 114; Patricia Caulfield 120; Ron Winch 141. Wildlife Unlimited, photographs by Tom McHugh, supplied by Photo Researchers Inc., N.Y.C.: 44, 60, 61, 135. Frank W. Lane, Pinner: Arthur Christiansen 15; Cecil Rhode 31; S. R. Pelling 73; Wilford L. Miller 74; Mrs J. R. Finch 99; Leonard Lee Rue III 95 bottom, 160, 198; Kirkpatrick Gallery of Photography 101. Mary Evans Picture Library, London: 17, 18, 171, 185, 188. Ardea Photographics, London: K. Fink 20; I. & L. Beames 23 top, 27; Su Gooders 23 bottom; P. Morris 54. Natural Science Photos, Watford: G. Kinns 28, 196. Naturfotograferna, Österbybruk, Sweden: Edvin Nilsson 29; Ove Andersson 37; Janos Jurka 115, 117.

Natural History Photographic Agency, Westerham: Brian Hawkes 40, 42 top; Andrew M. Anderson 83 bottom. Pitch, Paris: P. Montoya 41; Binos 50; M. Sester 53; G. Vienne & F. Bel 77; F. Gohier 80. Frank Roche: 56, 76. Eric Hosking F.R.P.S.: 70, 109. Cactus Clyde Productions, Maringonin, Louisiana: 75 bottom; Marty Stouffer 125; C. C. Lockwood 195. Jacana, Paris: Aldebert 78. P. Morris: 81. Tierbilder Okapia, Frankfurt a.M.: 142. British Museum, London: 144, 166, 181. Réunion des Musées Nationaux, Paris: 147. Department of the Environment: 148. The Zoological Society of London: 150, 151. Thomas Fall: 152, 153 top, 153 bottom, 154. Bibliothèque Nationale, Paris: 162, 187. Mansell Collection, London: 168, 170, 176, 183, 186. National Museum, Copenhagen: 178–179.

Line drawings

Contents page: from photo by James Simon; Bruce Coleman Ltd., Uxbridge. Title Page, 21: from photos by Leonard Lee Rue III; Frank W. Lane, Pinner. 11: from photo by P. Lefebvre; Pitch, Paris. 24: from diagram in *The Wolf*, © 1970 by L. David Mech, reproduced by permission of Doubleday & Co. Inc. 30: from chart in *Biology of Nutrition*, ed. R. N. T-W. Fiennes, © 1972 Pergamon Press Ltd., reproduced by permission of the publishers. 32: from photo by G. Kinns; Natural Science Photos, Watford. 35: from photo by Cactus Clyde Productions, Maringouin, La. 44: reproduced by permission of the Trustees of the British Museum (Natural History). 57: from photo by Tierbilder Okapia, Frankfurt a.M. 59: from diagram in *Biology of Nutrition*, ed.

R. N. T-W. Fiennes, © 1972 Pergamon Press
Ltd., reproduced by permission of the publishers; original version in 'The Ecosphere',
Scientific American, April 1958. 67: from photo
by Arthur Christiansen; Frank W. Lane, Pinner.
87: from photo by Karl Maslowski; Photo
Researchers Inc., N.Y.C. 96: from illustration
in *The Anatomy of Domestic Animals*, by Sisson
and Grossman, and reproduced by permission
of the publishers, W. B. Saunders Co. 98: from
graph in J. Clutton-Brock's article in *Science in
Archæology*, eds. Brothwell and Higgs,
published by Thames and Hudson, reproduced
by permission of author and publisher. 105:
from photo by Tom McHugh; Wildlife Unlimited. 133: from photo by W. L. Miller;
Frank W. Lane, Pinner. 145: from photo in
Eskimo Life in Alaska, © Alaska Publications.
175: from print in The Mansell Collection,
London. 193: from photo by Russ Kinne;
Photo Researchers Inc., N.Y.C.

Drawings for the endpapers, title page, facing
contents page, and chapter openings by Anna de
Polnay; maps by Phil Berry; drawings on pp. 32
and 44 by Jenny Richards; other technical
drawings by Jack Richards.

Index